The past is
Another
Country

VOLUME 2

12 STORIES BY NEW CANADIANS

WINNIPEG PUBLIC LIBRARY
2013

LIBRARY AND ARCHIVES CANADA CATALOGUING IN PUBLICATION

The past is another country : 12 stories by new Canadians.

ISBN 978-0-9869685-0-1 (v. 1).--ISBN 978-0-9869685-1-8 (v. 2)

1. Canadian literature (English)--Manitoba--Winnipeg.
2. Canadian literature (English)--21st century. 3. Immigrants'
writings, Canadian (English)--Manitoba--Winnipeg. I. Winnipeg
Public Library, issuing body

PS8257.W55P38 2011   C810.8'09712743   C2011-904048-4

Funding for this project has been provided in part by Citizenship and
Immigration Canada and Manitoba Immigration and Multiculturalism.

MIX
Paper from
responsible sources
FSC
www.fsc.org   FSC® C016245

"I can see the stars gathering, to lift you to a higher sky…"

—*Gentil Misigaro*

Table of Contents

Preface

What a thrill it is to be introducing the second volume of *The Past is Another Country*, a collection of twelve stories by twelve new Canadians.

The Finding Your Voice (FYV) creative life writing program for new Canadians began about seven years ago, in my living room, with a number of new Canadians with stories to share. Over time, the Winnipeg Public Library became our home, and gave us a place to meet and to grow to what it has become today. Our Saturday morning sessions at Millennium Library bring people from all over the world in an environment that empowers them to share their compelling stories of strength, resilience, and inspiring courage. The program builds bridges and creates opportunities for dialogue, breaks stereotypes and develops inter-cultural understanding. I am deeply grateful to have found shelter at the public library, a very suitable venue for such a program.

The FYV program puts the spotlight on the power of story and its ability to transcend boundaries and develop a sense of connection and empathy. The sharing of life stories is the essence of lifelong learning, builds bridges to better understanding, and defines the way we learn from one another. There is great interest in learning from each other and breaking through stereotypes about 'the other'. But sometimes fear gets in the way. The FYV program helps new Canadians break that fear and thrive in their new home country and within themselves as individuals, storytellers, and new writers. Invaluable friendships and connections are made through the sharing of stories and the unity created, building confidence and giving voice to transform lives. Inspiration is shared, giving belief that peace and personal empowerment are possible right here and right now—no matter what the past contained. It serves as a reminder that we are all in this world together.

The FYV program has received generous support from the Institute for Literacy and Transformative Learning at the University of Winnipeg, the Centre for Creative Writing and Oral Culture at the University of Manitoba, and Winnipeg Public Library. We have joined forces with the University of Winnipeg's Centre of Oral History and CKUW Radio to archive stories and produce radio episodes of interviews and stories by new Canadians. As well, funding for the printing of this book was provided by the Friends of the Winnipeg Public Library and Citizenship and Immigration Canada and Manitoba Immigration and Multiculturalism. Thank you all for your kind contributions.

A big thank you to Deborah Schnitzer, a personal hero of mine, for believing in a better world and for her brilliant mind and her big heart. Thanks to her class of amazing students at the University of Winnipeg, as well. These students raised money for this book by holding bake sales, a concert and a readathon because they too believe in the power of story, and how it contributes to a better world. For this connection, I am forever grateful.

Special thanks to Janis Pregnall for meticulously creating an impressive and thorough EAL activities section, making this book a unique and valuable resource to many. Thanks to Diana Janzen Ishigaki who benchmarked the stories too. Special thanks also to Quanhai Tonthat for capturing the essence of our authors and making it a memorable and fun photo shoot. To Nina Singh, one of the authors in this collection and now co-facilitator of the FYV program, thank you for bringing boundless creativity, thoughtful contributions, and tireless efforts and diligence in doing everything possible to make the FYV program what it is today.

My most profound gratitude and thanks goes to Kathleen Williams and Chris Laurie of the Millennium Library for providing continued resources and supports too numerous to mention.

The FYV program continues to be a great passion of mine because of the immense learning opportunities. I have traveled the world through these new writers and continue to be moved and inspired by their voices. This really is a dream come true for me and for all of the contributing writers. We couldn't be doing any of this without the support of the Winnipeg Public Library, Kathleen and Chris in particular, the 'awesomest' of awesome.

This is Finding Your Voice. This is *The Past is Another Country*. This is a better world. I am honoured to be a part of it.

JANINE LEGAL, is the founder and facilitator of *Finding Your Voice*; a freelance writer and community activist; Communications Coordinator for the General Child and Family Services Authority; Media Relations and Promotions Coordinator for Status4, an organization that provides free music and martial arts programs for inner city youth; and Executive Director of a *Better World Movement Inc.*, working to restore peace and building unity through the power of music and stories.

A Place Called Home

Lucy Kaikai

Home is where I was born. Where half the town knew my name, and my mother's name, and her mother's name. A neighbor was as good as a relative; adopted aunties, uncles, cousins and grandparents. The whole town was my playground. I knew every thicket and trail. For years I combed its sandy soil barefoot, exploring every corner. I climbed trees with my brothers, hunted termites with my friends and carved toys out of banana trees. From its soil I pulled up the perfect grass to make my very first doll and learned how to braid from its roots.

Home is where I scratched my grandmother's back by lamplight as she spun tales that could scare a ghost. Where I watched an eclipse in a basin of water and beat tin cups to scare the spirits into setting the moon free. My voice was sung hoarse in every church, every school, every stage. I danced under moonlit skies to the sound of beating drums and clapping hands. Like the vultures that circled overhead, I was present at every festival and masquerade. I saw passion in the eyes of men and felt their fiery embrace.

Home is where my plump thighs are called beautiful, not my skinny arms; a gap in your teeth and rings of fat around your neck are as desirable as dimples. A tan is never a fad and botox is unknown. Where women polish their skin with oil, prick their gums with a needle and call black beautiful. It takes many days to weave a piece of cloth that will multitask as a scarf or a dress or a skirt or a bag or even a snuggly. Home is a place where men cherish their mothers more than their wives and women adore their children more than their husbands.

Home is where every creature in the Atlantic ended up in my belly. The memories of deep-fried fish, crab soup and smoked oysters make my mouth water. Where rice is never boring. Not when it can be jollof rice, fried rice, check rice, 'wanpot' rice, coconut rice or 'pemahun.' Every leaf and every flower has the potential of becoming a delicious meal, made sumptuous with palm oil and maggi cubes. I learned how to plant a garden from trash and organic foods nourished my fast growing body that was unknown to growth hormones.

Home is where I walked countless miles along beaches, watched mighty waves crash a shoreline, witnessed indescribable sunsets. A land where I did not feel the heat of the sun because of the cool sea breeze. There I learned to swim in a river called black, whose

sketch by Lucy Kaikai

banks were lined with sand and rocks and pebbles. Laundry was a day's job. The river and rocks were my washing machine and the sun and pebbles my perfect dryer. Home is where I learned how to build a fire from coconut husks and twigs. I knew which homes always had a live coal or two I could borrow to build my own fire. I identified the perfect spot to build a house, high on a mountain top, with a view to take your breath away.

Home is where I was a majority. I was somebody and at the same time a nobody. Where my fame preceded my face and I was never asked how to spell my name. A place where my first name was never called without it being preceded by Baby, Mama or Granny. Where the notoriety of my ancestors made my last name famous. Home is where I knew the right words to say at the right time. Where nobody ever gave me a suspicious look or avoided my eyes. My greeting had never been met with silence and nobody chose to stand, rather than sit beside me on a bus. I was a daughter of the soil, at one with my surrounding, not a black dot on a white sheet.

Home is a place I fear I have lost and can never recover, shrouding my very soul with nostalgia. A place that only lives on in my heart. My footsteps have long been washed from the beaches I once combed. My name sandpapered from the wooden benches where it was once engraved. My perfect spot for a house probably belongs to another now. Where I long to return, yet fear cripples me. Fear that home will never be home again to my adulterous feet. I have been away too long. I no longer belong.

Now, my hope lies in the home Beyond the Blue, where I shall spend eternity. My voice will be united with angels to sing praises to my Maker and Redeemer. Home is where a mansion has been prepared for me on a street paved with gold. I shall be crowned with gems, robed with purity, and given sandals of peace. Wars will cease on every land. There will be no more sad partings and no broken hearts. Our colors shall fade into one, our gender will be of no significance and our boundaries will be washed away. A place where all my fears will vanquish and every longing fulfilled.

 **Lucy Kaikai** immigrated to Canada in 2004, under a Refugee Family Sponsorship Program. Before moving to Winnipeg, she lived in a refugee camp in the South East of Ghana for seven years. Lucy always seeks opportunities for personal growth and community development. In Sierra Leone, her country of origin, she worked as a volunteer in the Children's Department of the Korean Presbyterian Mission. While in Ghana as a refugee, she served with the Red Cross in Education and Sports programs. Her volunteer services in Canada have included being a friendly visitor at a personal care home and helping Newcomers with English at the Salvation Army's Multicultural Family Centre. She is a trained teacher who enjoys homeschooling her two children, preparing nutritious meals for her family, sewing and gardening.

Sierra Leone's boundaries give it a rough diamond shape on the west coast of Africa. It is bordered by The Atlantic Ocean, Guinea and Liberia. It's natural harbours made it a popular trading post both in goods and slaves in times past. Once known as the Athens of Sub-Sahara Africa, political corruption and lack of development earned it a place among the poorest countries in the world. Since it's independence from Britain in 1961, it has been mostly governed by greedy leaders. A civil conflict that lasted over a decade brought even more despair to an already impoverished nation and it's crumbling infrastructure. It's population of some five million inhabitants, is made of 12 indigenous tribes, the Krios, who are descendants of freed slaves and a large number of Lebanese and Indian merchants. Sierra Leone is a country of content people, spectacular beaches, majestic mountains, beautiful grasslands powerful rivers and fertile soil. Its mineral wealth includes gold, iron ore, titanium, bauxite and diamonds.

The Farewell

Briana Jeon

A beautiful song from the best singer flowed softly into my ear as sunshine tickled my toe. I knew it was time to wake up, but I just rubbed my face repeatedly with the covers. I felt so comfortable and snug, like I was on the clouds. I got up and drew the curtains and window open. The first thing I saw was a sparrow on the tree. It sang a beautiful song for me to wake up to. In time, the sparrow flew away, and I noticed the fresh air blowing with morning dew.

I heard my mummy and daddy's voices, and suddenly sounds of packing broke the peace of my beautiful morning. Ugh, right. Today we are moving. I tied my hair back into a ponytail, and checked my face to see if there was something on it. Then I was ready to see all my friends. First, I went to my boyfriend. He knew that I was moving. We always thought we were going to be parted someday, but we were not ready for farewell just yet. "I am sure you will do well there too. You will be a good adult," he said.

"I know long distance love is nonsense, it doesn't make any sense at all. So.."

We were too young, which means we didn't even know how to leave someone we love.

"I love you. Good bye."

We gave each other one last hug, shook hands, then I turned to go back home. It hurt, and one tear dropped onto my cheek. I stole my tears with the back of my hand, and made a fake smile, because I knew tears couldn't change anything. The past was past.

My daddy was waiting to take me home. He didn't say anything although he noticed that there was a tear on my cheek. The drive home was silent. What is love? I wondered. My dad had a vacant look on his face. My dad and I love each other so much, but there was something awkward between us. Maybe both of us thought it was easier to just remain quiet. However, when we arrived home, I held my dad's shoulder and gave him a good scolding for wanting to stay back alone in the city without us. He just smiled, then he cuddled me for a long time. I have always liked his cuddles. They make me forget every problem in my mind. I tried to say something more to him, but I had nothing to say anymore.

My mind felt empty. There was no one in front of my house. I called all of my friends and had a party the day before because I didn't want to see them on my last day. I didn't want to cry while holding them. I wanted to leave here with a smile, but now I realized that was my mistake. I already miss them so much.

We all went to the hospital to see my grandfather. He has idiopathic pulmonary fibrosis. His face goes pale easily even when he talks. Grandmother is taking care of him now, but she also forgets things easily. Whenever I go to her home, she asks me more than five times whether I ate dinner, although we had dinner together. They seemed so happy when I visited, so I feel sorry that I can't visit often because I live far from their house. Now I am moving even farther away than before. They looked blessed.

Suddenly I thought 'What if I never see them again?' I will not be here after graduating high school or university. Completing my studies will take about four to eight years. My grandfather looks so unhealthy now, and I was afraid that I would not be able to see his passing, or even come to his funeral. When I was in the hospital, I wasn't comfortable at all. One question didn't disappear from my mind. Am I doing the right thing? This is when I mostly cried. If I gathered all the tears that have dropped from my eyes, they would fill a cup. I will just call today a cry-day. I couldn't stop my tears from flowing anymore, so I just ran out of the room and rushed into the washroom. I have never cried like that before. I didn't want to show them my tears. I walked into the room again with a fake smiley face. I was sure that they were more upset than me. They didn't lose their beautiful smiles until I left.

I saw my home county through my eyes, and was imagining how Korea would look after many years. Yes, I think this is a good choice. This is a proper chance, and I think this is going to be good for me. I stepped forward, and there was a new world waiting for me.

BRIANA JEON had a happy life in South Korea. She enjoyed reading, especially fiction which took her into a fantasy world. She loves to look up at the sky with earphones in her ears and follow the planes. One day her parents decided that she needed to know how big the world was. They thought she needed a chance to be close to the world, so they asked her what she thought about moving to another country. She thought that they would move to a country like Australia, America, or England. She never thought she would come to Canada, but she came to Winnipeg when she was 15. She was shocked because she moved to Canada only two weeks after her parents told her. However, she is happy in Canada and is no longer homesick. Briana is now 17 (which is the best age ever) and is an 11th grade student at Dakota Collegiate, where she is studying Math and Business to be a good accountant.

SOUTH KOREA is also called The Republic of Korea. It has four seasons, and its winter is warmer than winter in Winnipeg. There are over 50 million people living in South Korea. Korea's map looks either like a tiger or a rabbit, depending on who is looking at it. Korea has many famous television dramas and musical personalities such as K-pop and YouTube sensation Psy (Gangnam Style). Korea is one of the strongest contributors to the IT and automobile world. Companies such as Samsung, LG, Hyundai and Kia all originated in Korea. Korea has many Karaoke bars, big shopping towns, public gyms, and amusement parks for teenagers to release their stress.

Winnipeg

Youngjoo (Julia) Kim

After an early dinner, we went outside wearing jumpers. We looked around with curiosity and fluttering hearts as we settled into a new place. Who are my neighbors? What's around my house? It was January 23, 2011, the second day we landed here. I left without my husband, for he is working in my home country. He was planning to come later. I came with my two daughters.

As soon as I opened the front door of my apartment, the cold air from outside pushed itself into the house like a baby rushing to its mummy. I stepped out. "Mom! It's too cold!", cried out my daughter. "Can we go back home now, please? I wanna go back to Korea. How can we live in a place like this?", cried out my daughter.

"Oh come on. Let's walk for only ten minutes. Isn't it nice that we can see the white world, and step on lots of snow?" However, we didn't walk for long. I realized that I couldn't even move my mouth. Shortly after, my body was frozen, so I couldn't walk anymore. I also worried for my children. I turned around with regret.

A few days after we arrived, I went shopping at St. Vital Mall with my kids for the first time. At six o'clock we went outside because the mall was closing. I didn't remember where I'd parked my car. I didn't' realize that there were so many doors in the mall. We tried to find the car for about an hour and a half, and our bodies were becoming frozen. It was getting dark and everyone was gone. Finally, I got help from a police officer so that I could find the car.

One fine winter afternoon I parked in front of my daughter's school waiting to drive her home. After a while, students poured out, and a few girls caught my focus. They ran out with only tank tops and no winter jackets, and enjoyed throwing snowballs at each other. Oh, my God! They made me delusional and I thought I was on a beach. After seeing this I put an overcoat on and turned the heater up in the car.

"Mummy, look at the sky! I love the blue sky and the white clouds. They are so pretty! I really wanna pick one of them and taste it, they look sweet and soft like marshmallows!" I raised my head and was dazzled by the beautiful sky. Sometimes my daughter's hobby is looking at the sky. Winnipeg's sunny sky seems to resemble a watercolor painting. Sometimes it tells a creative story with its clouds. Just like a fairy tale book.

I have now spent two winters and two summers in Winnipeg. In winter we have snow ball fights and enjoy outdoor skating. My children have adapted well as they always wear short shirts and do activities during winter. However, they can't only wear tank tops to go outside. Yet I can't lie down under the hot sun. I lie down under the shade of a tree and can feel the beauty and joy that summer gives us at the beach, and at the lake.

Sometimes I go to the library with my two daughters. We first started at the Louis Riel Library, which is near our house, but my favorites are the Millennium library downtown, St. Boniface, and St. Vital library. Every library has distinct characteristics, and unique images, so to me it isn't just going to a library, but so much more. The fact that I can return books to other libraries is another attraction which draws me to the library even more.

During the holidays we enjoy going to the park near our home. We prepare special sandwiches, snacks, and a cup of coffee to make me even more hyper. I play with my daughters like friends. We ride bikes and rollerblade.

There is no huge Disneyland, no department stores that stand in rows with flashy famous brands, no high buildings and no differently shaped apartments. But I love this quiet, beautiful, and small city named Winnipeg. I encounter lots of different cultures and colorful villages. I feel quiet, clean, and cozy. Winnipeg is coming close to my heart.

 **YOUNGJOO (JULIA) KIM** Youngjoo Kim is from Seoul, South Korea. She became a member of Shinhan Bank, where she worked in the personal changes, secretarial, and foreign exchange departments, and was a teller for 10 years. She made a new nest for herself in Pohang after she married, since her husband's company moved him there.

She immigrated to Winnipeg in January, 2011 with her two daughters and started a new life. She applied for permanent residence through the Manitoba federal government, because she was expecting to see her husband to join them in one year. However, she still does not have her permanent residence card, and her husband is still working in Korea.

It was lonely and hard for her at first since she was separated from her husband. However, she is now volunteering for personal and work experience as well as improving her English skills. She enjoys Canadian culture and is filling her insufficiency with good friends and joyful neighbors.

SOUTH KOREA is also called The Republic of Korea. It has four seasons, and its winter is warmer than winter in Winnipeg. There are over 50 million people living in South Korea. Korea's map looks either like a tiger or a rabbit, depending on who is looking at it. Korea has many famous television dramas and musical personalities such as K-pop and YouTube sensation Psy (Gangnam Style). Korea is one of the strongest contributors to the IT and automobile world. Companies such as Samsung, LG, Hyundai and Kia all originated in Korea. Korea has many Karaoke bars, big shopping towns, public gyms, and amusement parks for teenagers to release their stress.

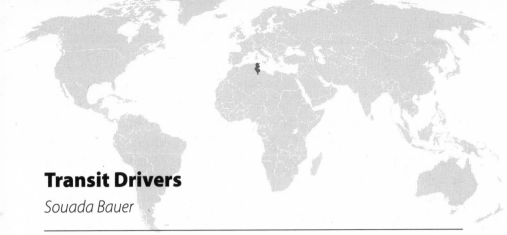

Transit Drivers

Souada Bauer

Transit drivers, ambassadors to be. Winnipeg transit drivers deserve a medal. At least some of them do. They are Manitoba's ambassadors to those on their new journey, seeking a path in the midst of muddy waters.

They have mastered the gift of interpretation of many languages. Watch them hand a transfer when suspecting the person simply forgot because it's not part of the bus deal somewhere else. Watch them exude patience with people crowding around them and asking them about a vague address. Listen to them reminding the person where to get off. How on earth do they remember that with all the traffic lights and stops!

Then you get the impatient kind who sees fit to vent their frustrations on someone who doesn't understand half of what they are saying. One driver told the passenger, "Lady, things just don't work this way here." The thing was she had no clue what he was talking about. His rant simply remained a rant, because we all feel the rant vibes and clam up in a matter of seconds.

Let me not forget to mention a rare type you don't see often, your security type of drivers. I thought newcomers were "targeted", having every bus pass checked ever so closely as in a border crossing. But what I noticed is that it's not only newcomers, but also homegrown people being scrutinized and every bus pass being scanned by eagle eyes. I feel relief and get off the bus to breathe in the free for all prairie air with no power hour limit.

Did I somehow overlook the speedy type? I've got a short story to tell. For a period of time at an unspecified location, I took the bus to the Collège de St. Boniface (Now Université de St. Boniface) to awaken the dormant French within me. I had barely placed my foot on the bus step when our eager driver sped off. I believe I must've prayed in as many languages as my mind could fabricate to get on and get off safely. I figured he must have been on a mission to get us to our final destination. But I only wanted to get to the college and parlé Français.

Buses come and go, but I haven't seen our eager driver on that line after my few heart stopping experiences. My destination remained the Collège de Saint Boniface. Suffice it to say, I was thankful.

Lo and behold, I saw him again. My mind started racing again to retrieve protection prayers stored in its files. But hey, there seemed to be a touch of patience in the driver's maneuvering of the bus. He isn't as he used to be.

While I was reflecting on speed and life, someone told the driver to slow it down even a bit more.

 SOUADA BAUER lives in Winnipeg. She is an EAL teacher at Entry Program and Mosaic-Newcomer Family Resources Network. She also co-facilitates in some Mosaic Family Programs. She speaks Arabic, French and English. She is climbing one of them thar hills of life with a youthful zest. She loves imbibing words with a touch of Keats, Rumi and Khalil Gibran.

Window of Dreams

Jamie Morales

"There are more opportunities abroad, higher standards of living,..." my opponent argued. I tuned out and looked into the green, tropical landscape beyond the classroom window. That was in year 2005, during a classroom debate about working abroad versus serving one's home country. I argued against leaving because I knew nothing of the poverty that had struck my country for generations. We weren't rich, but being an only child, I was sheltered. I was against my parents' decision to migrate to Canada. I was happy where I was. I was young, carefree, and naive. Seven years later, I now stand before a floor-to-ceiling window in an old high-rise condominium unit in downtown Winnipeg; gazing at the nightlights, the cars, and the sparkling snow. I couldn't be happier.

The good things went so that better things could come. Every morning, I wake up eager to go to university and learn from my professors and classmates alike. I never saw myself attending university outside of our old hometown, let alone in another country. I never thought I would one day be here, striving for top marks side by side with students from different parts of the world. It's wonderful. In the community, I meet passionate individuals who strive to make a difference every day. They do in many fascinating areas like entrepreneurship, leadership and communication, and literacy. It's inspiring to be around them. That's another great thing about being here; I can come face to face with people I admire. Imagine that. I live in the prairies, a place where the skies are wide open, the winds are strong, and where you can stand in the same spot the whole day and see both the sunset and the sunrise. I've only known dry and wet seasons in the first nineteen years of my life. Here, I can watch the snow fall, the ice melt, and the leaves change colors, firsthand. I can see the fog when I breathe out. I can touch the snowflake when it falls straight from the sky. Having said all that, the little things still count the most. There's food on my plate. I have warm clothes and embraces to wrap myself in. I have friends and love. I have a family I can come home to. I am very, very fortunate.

Better doesn't mean it's easy though. It's a misconception that life in Canada is a bowl of cherries. I've seen people juggle two or three jobs to make ends meet and to be able to support family back home. I know lawyers from back home who have worked call center jobs here. I've met MBA's, architects, and accountants who gave up good-paying jobs in their home country to be here. They've tried mopping floors, changing bed sheets, and flipping burgers. I know my mother has. We all struggle. We all start from the bottom again, sometimes lower. My mother insists on walking eleven blocks all year round, including winter, to and from work, to save money. My fifty-year-old father works eight hours a day assembling tractors whose parts are probably nothing less than ten pounds. A friend of mine, younger than I am, works nine hours a day out in the freezing winter doing construction. We do earn dollars, but we spend dollars too. We do have cars, not for luxury but for necessity. It's not easy to ride the bus with groceries in your hand during -40 degree weather. We do have healthcare but we dutifully pay a great deal of taxes. There are still people lacking in food, clothing, education, and shelter in Canada. It's still Earth.

Time flies here with our busy lives and hectic schedules. Before you know it, the younger kin you left back home have grown-up and grown old. They're not so little anymore. They don't need you as much anymore. The loved ones you miss so much have gotten used to not having you there. You wish that you could have spent more time with them when you had a chance. You wish you'd been there when they needed you to be. Some bonds grow stronger, some wither with the seasons. But then again, life goes on. It must.

The trials are inevitable. After all, we don't know what people are capable of until we put them to the test. At one point, our family had to be extremely frugal because our expenses exceeded our family income. I couldn't afford a dollar-and-twenty-five-cent drink in school. Yes, we did survive but that's not the hard part. The hard part is when you want to help your loved ones so badly but you just can't because you can't even help yourself. You just hope to God that they would understand and that they would somehow find a way through, even without needing your help. There will be people too, who will envy or discourage you, who will tell you that you can't do something because they can't do it themselves. The worst thing you can do is to listen. Protect your dreams no matter what, from everyone, especially from yourself. There will be heartaches and disappointments. There will be sacrifices you have to make. They all will make the journey tough, exquisite, and worthwhile. Pain can be a beautiful thing, if you use it well.

We had to give up many things to be here. We had to give up security, relationships, home, and a thousand other dreams. We had to start life all over again. I gave up that green tropical landscape I saw that day for these boundless horizons that lay before me tonight. I have no regrets. For every dream that we dream, a thousand others fade. For every dream that we live, a thousand others die.

JAMIE MORALES is just another fine dreamer who is head over heels in love with writing, living, and learning. She is an only child to Jaime and Nena Morales, whom she describes as the two most loving parents in the world. She grew up in the province of Isabela, a common pathway of tropical storms in the Philippines. Jamie and her parents moved to Canada when she was eighteen years old. She is currently pursuing a combined major in Applied Computer Science and Business Administration at the University of Winnipeg. She hopes to pursue parallel careers in serial entrepreneurship and academia.

The PHILIPPINES, also known as the Pearl of the Orient Seas, is a Southeast Asian archipelago of over 7,000 islands. The country has one of the richest biodiversity in the world, the fifth largest coastline, and approximately 170 languages. The tasty Filipino cuisine is a product of Spanish, Chinese, American, and other Asian influences. The strongest of Filipino values include respectfulness to elders, religiousness, solidarity of the family, and hospitality.

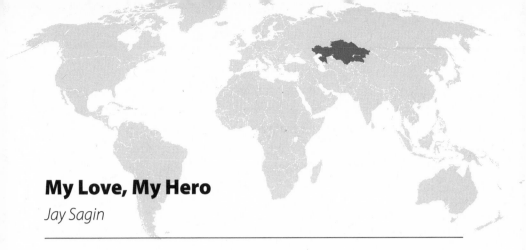

My Love, My Hero

Jay Sagin

"Do you want a painkiller to help with the pain?" asked the doctor.

"No, I will bring my baby into the world without it," replied my wife.

"Are you sure? We will not give any painkillers during the birth", the doctor tried to convince my wife.

"Yes, I am sure," replied my wife, as she squeezed my hand, asking me for support.

I was holding my wife, and she was squeezing my hand when she was preparing to give birth to our baby. I asked my wife why she did not take the painkiller. She replied that she worried a lot about the baby. She said that if something happened during the birth, I must be more concerned about our baby than I was about her. She said that she was ready to give her life for the baby. I tried to calm my wife down by kissing her and saying that everything would be alright. I was repeating that I love her and our baby and that I was here to guard them both. We were waiting for several hours. I tried to be near my wife all of the time. I tried to calm her down by hugging and kissing her. My hands were on my wife's belly and I felt all the movements of our baby inside her.

Suddenly, the baby started to move, and my wife screamed in pain. I was holding my wife, and my wife was squeezing my hand with her fingers. I tried to help my wife, but her body was filled with pain. Our baby was trying to come out, and all movements created pain for her. I wished some of the pain could be transferred from my wife to me. She was screaming, and her body was sweaty. I felt my wife's pain when her nails were squeezing and cutting the skin on my hands. Tears were falling from my eyes.

"Push! Push! Push!" the doctor directed my wife. My wife was pushing and pushing for some minutes.

The baby's head appeared, and the baby started to squeal. The baby was so gorgeous!

When the baby was out, the doctor gave me scissors, and I cut my baby's umbilical cord.

My wife and I were so happy to have our newborn baby!

My wife and I were smiling, crying, and holding the baby. We felt that we loved each other and our baby very much.

We had waited for this baby for many years. We planned our family, and we planned our expenses. We saved money to buy a home, and we bought one when the baby was ready to be born. We checked our health for many years. We dreamed of creating a new life, but we were concerned that we had to create a new life responsibly. We thought that we should give our baby the best that we had in both of us. Our baby is the creation of our love: my wife's love and mine.

I love my family. I love my wife. My wife is my hero!

 JAY SAGIN   My name is Jay Sagin. I am a mathematician-environmentalist and I am trying my best to live life and be in balance with nature. I am trying to compute, predict and plan everything in my life as much as I can. I respect nature and I am trying to understand, study, and predict natural events. That is why I have studied geological science with natural resource and environmental management.

My expertise is in the application of Remote Sensing and Geographic Information Systems in hydrologic and hydraulics modeling with comprehensive mathematical analyses. I was born in a rural, nomadic countryside near Mongolia, in Kazakhstan. From my childhood I lived in the small nomadic yurt, which is similar to the First Nation's, Native—Canadian yurt. I love nature. I love people, my family and my kids. I am a friend and student who is still trying to understand his best friend: nature.

My country of origin is **KAZAKHSTAN**. Kazakhstan is very similar to the Canadian Prairies. It has similar weather and vast, flat areas of steppe grasslands. The Canadian Prairies remind me of my lovely childhood. My mom had a hard time trying to put clothes on my body when I was a child, or to convince me to wear anything. She remembered that I was a happy boy and that I would often run away from school and home. It took a considerable amount of time for my mom and my first childhood teacher to instill the desire to learn in me. I felt my mom's love all the time, even if I did many wrongs. I now have my own kids, and I want to create the same environment for my kids that I had in my childhood. I want my kids to feel that their home is full of love.

El Dorado

Nina Singh

In order to write a story you must first be prepared to lie. Fabrication is no longer reserved for the likes of the Monarchy, Governments and other nobility. The places and events which I am about to describe to you are not real.

Once upon a time there was a little girl who loved stories. Her mother told her every night about the tale of the Golden City. The little girl would listen eagerly for hours as her mother told of the magical place where people dined on the finest foods by candlelight. Their houses were all velvet red and their streets were lined with the most exotic fruits. Their ruler was so favored that he was given precious gifts from Kings all over the world. The little girl's mother had been there, and so had her grandmother and her mother before that. Sometimes she chanced to see a strange look in her mother's eyes. Eyes that she wished she had. Her mother had given her replicas of every part of herself, except for her eyes. Her mother had the eyes of an exotic empress. Ones that hid secrets and had the power to bewitch. The little girl thought her eyes boring since the only thing they matched was the ocean, whose water reflected the blue skies that lingered above.

Whenever she listened to her mother's story, she would escape into her own world. A world where she was one of the lucky children in that land miles across the waters blue. The little girl lived far away from the Golden City, but close enough to see it glittering like an undiscovered jewel in the distance. Her kingdom was not quite as nice, but it did have the most magnificent tower. In it was her rather large family. Each member was quite different, probably owing to their experiences of traveling to far off countries all around the world. Yet they loved each other in spite of their incessant babbling. She would fall asleep every night while staring at the enchanted kingdom from her window. The little girl vowed that one day she too would go to that place. That place of secrets and gold.

I was just a child and like so many of us, I only heard what I wanted to hear. My mother tried her best to shield me from the horrifying reality, but we all grow up, and with that comes the ability to decipher. The truth is we lived in a dark, hideous tower. One that was infested with rats and reeked of bodily waste. I say "we" because there were so many people crammed into every twist and turn. Everyone spoke different languages so life was frustrating since we could not understand each other. We were shipped here by those in the Golden City. They drove us to this place because we did not belong in their precious world. Oh but they needed us. They needed us to fight their wars, build their land and do their dirty work. They needed us to keep their Golden flag flying.

We didn't always live in a tower; we used to live off the land, but that all changed when it began to happen. The tower was built to escape the blood curdling screams from the restless souls that haunted the land below. Ghosts of the murdered and condemned. Ghosts from the 'dark' continent. Ghosts of the so-called 'barbarians' from the Middle East. Ghosts of the Chinese Railway workers. Ghosts of the people turned to dust in Nagasaki. Ghosts of those who drowned in the merciless sea of trying to find a better life. Then there were the ghosts below the land. Ghosts of those who were here first, and who will never forget the pain of their calculated genocide.

The tower was a fiendish concoction. It had the outline of a dying old man, whose spine was painfully curved and about to crack. The bottom of the tower housed the cripples. They cried out every day in agony. They had no backbones you see, they sacrificed them all to build the Golden City. Over time some in the tower slowly began bartering for necessities. Through this, they started to understand each other's language and value their beliefs. But some refused to make eye contact. They hopelessly held on to the memory of their homeland like a mother who is unable to let go of her dead child. They mourned incessantly for the traditions of their abandoned motherland. A motherland that would not recognize the children of her soil if they ever dared to return.

There were women who came back and had babies. However, the babies no longer looked like them. Their features were different and their skin and hair were lighter. Many of these women came back depressed and detached from all others around them. They didn't want to see their babies and screamed bitterly in the middle of the night. Those women locked themselves in the dark room at the top of the tower. Then there were the men who never came back. Men who said to their wives they would be back soon, but never returned to the decaying tower of hopeless babblers. Many wives went by the ocean's edge every day for the rest of their lives hoping they would see the familiar face that never came home.

I am in that place. That place of cruelty and deception. That place where they stole our fruit trees and exploited our people. That place where they display our belongings in gilded buildings as if they were theirs. That place where the only aid they send are boxes of M-24's to further corrupt the world. That place where peacemakers sign the agreement with one hand and bludgeon you with the other. That place where they know nothing of dyes so they stained their houses red with the blood of our people. That place where you are welcomed with open arms, as long as you always know your place. That place where you soon realize that multiculturalism and post-colonialism do not exist. That place where they let you freeze if you do not have exact change. That place where nothing is given without a price. The place you would do anything to come to, including strip naked to let a doctor determine that your body is not diseased or defective. The place where their elderly die alone because they are no longer useful. A place where you bleed every day from stepping on the sharp, shattered pieces of your former self. A place where they study and champion the theories, practices and histories of our people to make themselves feel better for what they have done and continue to do. A place like this.

I wish I had never come. If only I had stopped my silly daydreaming and listened to the true story of my mother. That strange look in her eyes was one of fear and urgent warning. As I look in the distance I see the ship. The ship that must have brought so many, either by force, trickery, or choice. My heart was ripped out of my chest with one blow. I wanted to scream, but what was the point? They are bringing my daughter.

 **NINA SINGH** At first glance the looking glass reflects a single image that is not a true reflection of oneself. Look closer and you will see the many faces and experiences that have made you who you are.

Mommy, you are my inspiration. My family, you are my dysfunctional place of comfort. My friends, you are the sharers of my memories and occasional lapses of insanity. Curtis, you are my love. Thank you all for giving me precious parts of myself.

GUYANA Sir Walter Raleigh journeyed to South America in 1595 in search of the Golden City of El Dorado. He was convinced that *his* city of treasure would be found within the 'primitive' and 'undiscovered' land of Guiana (now Guyana). His expeditions were failures and his accounts gross fabrications. El Dorado is still there. It becomes illuminated every day, as it always has, by the rays of Guyana's golden sun.

Canadian Sonata

Sergio Roysen

Home. The Map.
Easy definition.
Impossible task.
Coordinates:
The upper part of your chest.
The right side of your brain.
The fists that you make with your hands.
Rules:
If you feel,
It's because it's absent.
If you create,
It's because it doesn't exist.
If you fight,
It's because it's not yours.
Instructions:
Feel,
look through the closest wall.
Smell the wind that is not blowing.
Kneel, put your ear to the ground and hear.
Because it's approaching.
Create,
chain yourself to a cloud and fly.
Touch the shadow of the night,

Shut yourself off from the crowd.
Because it's waiting.
Fight,
let the pressure on your eyes blind you.
Shake the tremors of your shoulders and advance.
Inhale. Exhale. Inhale. Explode.
Because it's worth it.
And because by now,
You really don't have a choice.

 **SERGIO ROYSEN**   Delusional person who landed in Canada in February of 2010, searching for that ever eluding state: happiness.

ARGENTINA   South American country with a history sometimes difficult to accept or swallow.

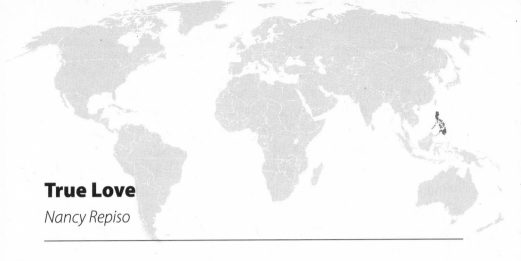

True Love

Nancy Repiso

On August 11, 2008 I landed in Winnipeg. At that moment, I started to dream and value life even more. While I was enjoying the country's four seasons, especially the snowflakes on Christmas day, a lot of life's learning happened. With it came experiences that I am thankful for because they made me stronger, more aware, and sensitive to other's feelings. They helped me stand on my own and believe in myself.

There was a point when I thought my life was almost perfect, yet I felt that there was a part of me that was missing. I was missing that special someone with whom I would spend the rest of my life. I know that filling that missing part requires more than a wish, a desire, hope or dream. One has to first grow beyond their limitations as a person. Preparing yourself for a relationship helps to encourage the essence of true love.

Coming to Canada awakened the possibility of finding him. One day while walking towards work, I talked to God telling him that I am emotionally ready to meet 'him'. I had already conditioned myself for that awaited moment. To be honest, I was dreaming of a good-looking, rich, professional and intelligent guy. But my few years of staying in Canada made me realize that finding someone with those qualities wasn't what would make our relationship last forever. I realized that those qualities were just the outer part of a person. My perception suddenly changed. I asked God instead for someone who will love, trust and respect me until our final heart beats. I knew in my heart that whoever he was, he was worth the wait. I believe that God created a specific person meant just for me and that he will find ways to connect us.

On my way home, I received a text message from my friend telling me that her childhood friend invited me on a well-known social network called Facebook. I accepted the invitation. His name is Edwin and he has been living in Japan for eight years where he works as a welder. We started to communicate and eventually saw each other through Skype and Yahoo Messenger. We slowly started to know each other until we became completely comfortable. Edwin and I shared our ups and downs as well as our experiences that we had in other countries. We became good friends. Living our lives away from our families and friends motivated us to value each other more and appreciate what we have. At that time, a Tsunami and earthquake hit Japan. I found myself praying for him since I was concerned about his situation.

After one month, I suddenly remembered the special prayer given to me by a friend – a special prayer on how to find the right person. I prayed that prayer for a month. It was effective. Our communication became consistent and deeper on a more personal level. I saw myself in him and him in me. A small voice in my head told me that he was someone special. He is exactly the one that I've been praying for. In one of his messages, he said, "Honestly, I saw in you all the characteristics that I am looking for in my future wife." At that moment I felt something really different, something beyond my comprehension, a deep sense of love between us. After a few months we both decided to be in a relationship. I did think that a long distance relationship might not work out, especially considering that we had never met each other. Some people say that a thing like this is impossible, but we both understand and respect what they feel. It's hard to explain to them that when you find the right person, you just know deep inside your heart that they're the one for you. Like other couples, we have also experienced bad moments but they don't last for long. We never allow them to ruin the foundation that we have built. No matter what happens, our love conquers all.

He surprises me with gifts and flowers. In January of 2012, there was a small yellow paper bag that he specifically told me to open in front of him via Skype. I was shocked and speechless when I saw what was inside the box. It was a ring. Then he immediately said what every woman desires to hear when they fall in love "Will you marry me?" I paused for a bit, trying to let it all sink in. Then I answered, "Yes". That was the happiest day of my life and I couldn't believe it was happening. My world stopped for a moment and I had to ask myself if I was dreaming. I wished that if I were dreaming, God wouldn't wake me up. But no, it was not just a dream.

One time in June 2012, during our conversation, he mentioned that he sent a letter to me for our anniversary. He advised me not to open it until he was at home. I was excited opening my mailbox every day, but there was no mail from him and it was two days before our anniversary. I lost hope of getting his letter on time for our special day. Then I slowly walked towards our house, and opened the door where a big box welcomed me, a box full of my favorite foods and letters. I checked who it came from and I started to smile while reading his name. I can't thank God enough for making my life complete. Life has lots to offer, but sometimes we're just scared to take risks. We'll never know what is out there unless we try to find it.

I became more excited as we started to plan for our wedding. We're both going home to finally meet each other. I can't wait for my special day when I'll put on the most amazing white dress I could ever imagine. A day when all my loved ones will gather to witness the beginning of my life's journey with him. A day when I'll be standing on a sacred place filled with music, flowers and decorations. But everything doesn't really matter at all, because the only thing that matters to me is one man - the person waiting for me at the end of the aisle, looking at me the way I look at him. True love connects the two of us together despite the distance. This testifies that God is still in control of everything. Just put your trust in God alone and you'll see. Things will fall into place.

Like stories on television, books, movies and fairytales, I want you to know that true love really does exist.

 My name is **NANCY REPISO**. I was born and raised in the Philippines. My father passed away when I was 12 years old and my mom lives with my brother in Virginia. I am the youngest of eight siblings. I attended De La Salle University for a Computer Secretarial course and graduated as Most Outstanding Secretary of the Year. Moving to Winnipeg, Canada was one of the major decisions I made in my life, but living here has helped me to grow and develop both in my personal and professional life. I was inspired by the kind of life we had before, so I told myself that nothing could stop me from achieving my dreams. Life has ups and downs but don't let them ruin your plans. Instead, take that as motivational material for you to start seeing the brighter side that life has to offer. My life's principle is to always do your best in whatever you believe will make you happy. If things don't work out the way you planned or exactly the way you imagined, trust me, even better will come. We can only live once in this lifetime so let's make the most out of our stay.

PHILIPPINES is a tropical country that has a tropical rainforest climate. It consists of more than 7100 islands. These islands have a lot to offer to tourists and to Filipinos alike, such as historical sites, beautiful sceneries, beaches, churches and museums. But one thing that separates us from the rest of the world is our colorful and lively culture. Most provinces have their own identity. Filipinos are friendly and known for their trademark hospitality. That's why tourists keep visiting the country. Another cultural value that we have is the so-called "close family ties", where a level of closeness is practiced effectively everyday. Philippines is known for having the world's longest and merriest Christmas season. This is the most awaited celebration. The Spirit of Christmas starts in September and lasts until the Feast of the Three Kings. During this season, we have an early morning mass that begins formally on December 16th and ends on the 24th. Streets are usually filled with colorful lights, lanterns "parol", houses with different Christmas decorations, and children who sing carols to their neighbors. We have Noche Buena where family, friends, relatives and neighbors drop by to greet each other "Merry Christmas or Maligayang Pasko". Philippines has lots to offer, so come visit and have fun.

More than an Immigrant: the remaking of self within a culture of silence

German Cruz Reyes

I've been living in Canada for five years. When I was landing in Winnipeg I wasn't concerned or aware of the implications of being an immigrant. The mentioned culture clash, cultural identity, stereotypes, discrimination and racism did not seem important in that moment. Naïvely I thought, 'how hard could it be living in another culture?' and to speak another language, to adapt and understand other values and contexts? I said to myself "no big deal everything is the same no matter where you live… right? Sure!" Maybe in some ways, but that's not one hundred percent true.

At some point, that is hard and exciting to remember, the reality came to me. Suddenly I woke up in the middle of the night and found myself walking around my small apartment, looking through my window into another window, don't ask me why, but I began to understand the feeling of claustrophobia.

My worries of living here, and my need to, broke my bubble and took me out of my comfort zone. Worries like learning another language (or let's be precise, speaking another language) were, and still are, extremely hard. I developed a high tolerance for frustration and learned how to laugh at myself. At times, this process was even fun. The first couple of years I couldn't avoid feeling like I was a monkey, especially when I came across very condescending people along the way who looked and spoke to me very slowly, like I was sort of stupid. "Oh he doesn't speak English." Howww arrre youuu? Niice tooo meeeeet youuu." Or, other occasions when people asked me a question, yet they spoke while looking at my wife instead of me. This happens even now. That was hard to take with a forced smile, "Come on, I am smart. Just because I don't speak English doesn't mean that I am stupid, use your common sense!" I said in silence not to lose my cool.

I have experienced many situations like this in a very short period of time while living here. I understood that it was a process and that I had to learn English faster, especially if I wanted to find a job - a stressful matter that makes many immigrants sweat and feel colder (even in winter time).

Finding a job wasn't easy. With very limited and 'broken' English I didn't have many options to choose from. These new circumstances saddened my optimistic attitude however, as an immigrant you don't have time or the privilege to feel sorry for yourself. You just have to keep going.

Finally an employer of a major warehouse company called and gave me a job after the hardest two interviews that I have ever had. Interviews which included the very awkward question: "how many times in the year do you get sick?" In that moment I didn't realize the oppressive connotation of that question. I mean I was still naïve and grateful to have the opportunity to work and because somehow you believe that you have to prove something extra.

In that moment, I didn't understand this kind of culture of silence. The work environment was hostile from the moment I crossed the door. I could feel it in the energy. Everyone was stressed out trying to make the productivity because the supervisor was pushing by saying "let me remind you that you are in your probation time". Everyone was rude; understandable I guess when everyone is trying to survive.

In any other situation, I would have already found my way to the door, but that was the most vulnerable time in my life. Besides being isolated, with no community, no English, I was expecting my first baby. I had to be a good provider, husband and father. For that reason, I tolerated the situation and worked very hard, harder than I've ever worked, but without notice or warning, exactly one day before my six months probation time was due, and on my wife's birthday, they laid me off. "Perhaps you are not the kind of person for this job"—sure and it took you six months to find that out eh. That day my feet were heavy, I came home feeling miserable, and hopeless that I even forgot the back and muscle pain that I was carrying with me.

For the first time I opened my eyes and understood the "friendly labour culture in Canada"—the negative one. And for the first time I asked myself "what am I doing here?" Fortunately, I found the answer when I looked at my beautiful wife carrying our daughter. However, I couldn't help feeling angry, humiliated, abused and exploited. It was totally ridiculous: six months probation time without benefits and paying into the union close to five hundred dollars without their protection. If this was not a manipulative system and exploitation, what was it?

Later I found out that this company does this sort of thing all of the time. They hire many immigrants and make them work harder with the threat of failing their probation time with full intention to just give the contract to one employee out of many. Sadly this can happen to anyone, but for some reason I think this most often happens to immigrants. In some ways this is legal. That is discrimination.

Coming through these experiences as an immigrant, I started to see how discrimination and racism against immigrants exists in Canada. Obviously you don't hear this openly, because according to Canadian culture you are not allowed to complain. It is not politically correct. I have seen this culture of silence in the schools and even when I'm out for dinners with friends.

If you repeat this statement some people can get uncomfortable or even upset and pretend that you didn't say anything or will say Canada is multicultural and so friendly to immigrants, or they will even go so far as to ask you why you are in Canada. It is true that Canada respects other cultures; however, racism and discrimination do exist. Just because racism doesn't manifest itself in physical violence, doesn't mean it doesn't happen here. Racism is hiding within the culture of silence. Because it is not open or politically correct to say something against another culture makes this kind of discrimination and racism more mentally stressful. If it were more open, at least you would know what to expect. But in this case you don't know and can't be sure when someone is being condescending if in fact they are being racist.

Sometimes I believe that racism and discrimination are intrinsic to human nature. In my experience, people have criticized me for my way of speaking English and have insulted my background with their 'funny jokes.' These incidents that happened here are not only coming from older, white Canadian generations—they are coming from many other cultures and races as well. Some people do it unconsciously: they don't realize the racism that is implicit in the things that they say. Others do it because they have some kind of an inferiority complex.

Self-racism and discrimination between immigrants is even more aggressive and demonstrates a lack of cultural identity. Sometimes you see immigrants pretending that they are white Canadians and they discriminate against other immigrants without knowing that this is part of the mental colonization against marginalized cultures, perpetuating the supposed superiority of the dominant culture. Racism between immigrant groups just perpetuates the inequalities prescribed by the dominant culture and legitimizes the supposed superiority of one culture over another. This is an act of violence that creates segregation. We are proud of multiculturalism in Canada, this is Canada's identity and culture, but at the same time we employ closet racism and discrimination. Does this make sense?

I think we have to see the things that we have in common and celebrate the differences, because the differences make us unique and culturally rich. I am stating this because I think it is important to mention that this has been part of my experience. Also, I believe that it is important to express that I came here for love and that has helped to keep me grounded. Even though I wasn't expecting to encounter difficulties, I have also found love for Canada. The experience of living here has also been positive.

One thing that impressed me when I arrived in Winnipeg was how wonderful it was to see people from all over the world with different backgrounds. Living in relative harmony, in some ways we are building a new world community. In the end we are all humans. That intrinsically makes us share the same world, and similar struggles in life. Pay the bills, find a job, worry about the future, protect the environment, adapt to a new culture, learn a second, third or fourth language, build a new cultural identity accordingly. I guess we can't have more in common than this.

The cultural clash that I experienced moving to Canada has changed my personality and cultural identity. So many times it was hard to understand and see myself within Canadian culture. Finding myself amongst all these social preconceptions about immigrants and my ideas about Canada, wasn't easy, especially during the first years when feeling like an outsider without context, without meaning and with the word immigrant that is so general that it doesn't mean nor express anything about you.

When I visited my parents in Mexico, I realized how much I'd changed. I could not see myself any longer living in the land where I was born, and at times 1 felt awkward in the old house. Surprisingly I found myself sitting on the peak of the mountain seeing two different realities. Canada and Mexico have become a part of my cultural identity and a part of who I am.

In conclusion, I think everyone has their own personal culture and way in which they interpret the world as well as their broader cultural identity. When you move to another country, the puzzle that you relatively had together, is now all over the place. We have to rebuild the puzzle and it isn't easy. The pieces are not only all over the place, they are now different and don't fit in the same places they used to fit before.

Your personal and cultural identity has changed. You have to break the stereotypes, adapt to different values and ways to interpret life. It is not easy. You have to pass through a lot of frustration, misunderstanding, and disappointment. Even worse, sometimes you have to get past being patronized, endure condescending remarks, being excluded and discriminated against.

After a while or according to your attitude, your Canadian identity develops—all of this without losing your background. That will always be a part of you. However, we have to accept that now we are different, not the same person with the same ideas and values that we had before moving here. Not better, not worse, just different. This is the beauty of Canada and the reason why I love Canada and I am proud to be living here.

We need to break nationalist stereotypes that we are just where we were born. That's an external circumstance that we don't have control or choice over. It is amazing that as humans we have the opportunity to choose what and where we want to be. Canada respects this freedom. As immigrants we make Canada richer and Canada makes us richer. We make Canada and Canada makes us. *We* are now Canada.

GERMAN CRUZ REYES is originally from Nezahualcoyotl, a city of approximately 1,232,565 people, just outside of Mexico City. Raised in a large, traditional Mexican family headed by two loving parents, German is one of three brothers and three sisters. With his mother being from Michoacán and his father indigenous to Oaxaca, German represents a blend of both indigenous and "mestizo" Mexican identity. After meeting his Canadian wife in Mexico City in 2006, German immigrated to Canada in 2007 to be married. In 2009 they were blessed with a daughter, Valentina, representing his roots officially finding their place in Canadian soil.

A lover of philosophy, athletics, and family life, German is also a keen observer of the nuances in Canadian life, the transformation of his identity as a Mexican living in a Canadian context, and the unique challenges represented by the promise of multiculturalist ideals embedded in Canadian culture. When not caring for his three-year-old daughter, German currently makes a living by supporting individuals with disabilities to live in the community. He hopes one day to work as a personal trainer until he can open up his own business here in Winnipeg.

MEXICO, so much more than any packaged beachside vacation. Mexico is very rich in natural resources and culture, full of contrasts, political resistance, values, traditions, social problems and corruption. "Oh poor Mexico, too far away from heaven and too close to the USA." But more than anything, Mexico is my family.

Spirits of the North

Faisal Islam

It had taken more than an hour from Fort Resolution to reach this remote outpost on the shore of the Great Slave Lake. The sun had just set but the immense sky was still filled with intense hues of red, orange and blue, interspersed by splashes of dark grey. It was early October and the night was descending on us quickly, blanketing the fiery forests of the fall.

"Here is our boat, just the kind you wanted" announced Fred Liske, my guide, without pointing to any particular direction or object.

Scanning the water's edge, I could make out the silhouette of a few wooden planks tied to some irregularly shaped poles. This must be the jetty from where we would depart. But there was no boat of any kind in sight.

Sensing my uneasiness, Fred waved towards a bushy area. A closer look revealed the outline of a canoe turned upside down. It was carefully camouflaged behind a thicket of horsetail and sedges along the edge of a dense, tall stand of spruce, alder and willow.

Leaving my gear by the trail for a moment, I helped Fred to turn the canoe over and push it through the grassy area all the way to the lake. Once on the water, the canoe came to life. It looked light but sturdy and ready for the mission.

"My old man built this canoe all by himself", said Fred, with a big grin on his face. "He made the body from birch barks and stitched them together with watape. Used pine resins to seal the joints." "What about the ribs and the gunwales?" I asked.

"White cedar", replied Fred. Even the paddles were carved from solid wood.

Super! I liked Fred's attention to details. I didn't want to hire a loud engine-boat that would shatter the peace and tranquility of this quiet northern evening.

We quickly loaded up the canoe. Fred settled for the bow seat, and looking over his shoulder, asked me to use the paddle to push the canoe away from the shore.

With a gentle hoosh, the canoe slid through the dark and glassy waters of the Great Slave. The distant calls of goshawks and grouses and the incessant chirping of the crickets gradually faded away behind a dense blanket of fog.

Soon the warm evening glow started to fade into a purplish grey backdrop against which the familiar stars began to emerge. Tonight, the moon would have a very late appearance, leaving the center stage to the more distant performers.

It would take a couple of hours to reach the tiny uncharted island we were heading for. This gave me plenty of time to take in the sights and sounds of this magical world. The lake now looked like a giant mirror mimicking the show that had begun to unfold on the vast canvas of a clear northern sky.

It was a stellar party. I had never experienced anything like it before. The brightest and closest performer hanging barely above the horizon was Jupiter, quickly gliding away towards the northeast exit. Capella, on the other hand, took a gentler course and lit up half the sky with its brilliance. The majestic Great Bear crossed the meridian in full grandeur with Hercules following its trail. Later that night, the Gemini twins looked particularly impressive. And who could miss Princess Vega, waiting for her lover Altair who, unable to cross the Milky Way, stood helplessly on the other side?

As we moved deeper into the lake, the beauty of the cold sub-arctic night took us over. I heard Fred chanting in a low voice but couldn't make out what he was saying. He was probably chanting in Chipewyan or Cree. Or, perhaps his old man had taught him the secret language the spirits of the north spoke. It seemed his soul had left his body and was dancing with the spirits into whose territory we had intruded.

Like an ancient mariner, Fred let the stars above guide and bring us to the uncharted island. The spot was just perfect, spacious and open, with no tall trees blocking the view. Fred gave me a hand in setting up a couple of sturdy tripods fitted with cameras. One was for mapping the star trails with a very long exposure; the other to capture the most magnificent show on earth: the dancing of the northern lights.

At first it was just a gentle glow here and there, which turned into intermittent flares of violet and blue more like fine mists of colors sprayed along the horizon. Soon bold strokes of yellow and green crisscrossed the sky. Turquoise-blue swirling eddies stretched for miles into the upper atmosphere. And flashing strokes of amber and red danced across the celestial dome.

The shape and size of those patterns were changing quickly and randomly. I focused on the northwest part of the sky, which seemed to be most active. Making a few quick adjustments to the settings, I began to shoot.

"Oh! Look at the throbbing blaze of purple, opal and gold!" Click, click click.

"Here comes the blue-white serpent again!!" Click, click click.

"Can't miss those rippling curtains shimmering across the sky!" Click, click, click.

The frenzy went on and on for over an hour before slowing down; only then did my heart-beat return to normal. My hands shook in excitement as I previewed some of the images. I was pleased with what I saw but no image could convey the intensity and beauty of what we had just experienced.

"Perhaps we should pack up now?" I asked Fred.

There was no immediate response from Fred. The glimmering northern lights revealed parts of his face; he looked spellbound and possessed. Now I knew what kept him coming back to this sacred place year after year.

Tomorrow, I would be flying back home and the thought of leaving this magical land saddened me. Suddenly, deep inside me I felt a warm and reassuring touch of the spirits of the north. I was not going home alone.

"Hey Fred, when are you gonna arrange the next round of trips?" I asked.

"Round Christmas and New Year. That's when most folks like coming here.

"Well, book me in!"

 Faisal Islam was born and brought up in Bangladesh. After completing his graduate studies in the US, he started his career as a university faculty in Bangladesh. Later on, he worked for a number of international developmental agencies and visited many countries in Asia, Europe and Africa. Faisal moved to Winnipeg in 2010 and initially taught at the University of Manitoba and the University of Winnipeg. Presently, he works full-time for the Province of Manitoba. In his spare time, Faisal enjoys reading, travel and photography.

Bangladesh is a South Asian country which became independent in 1971. It is situated in the north-eastern part of the Indian subcontinent, bordered by India, Myanmar and the Bay of Bengal. It is one of the most densely populated countries in the world with a population of around 152 million. The country is presently going through a transition from being an agricultural economy, towards a manufacturing and service based economy. Its main exports include ready-made garments, textile, frozen food, jute, tea, fertilizer, pharmaceuticals and ceramic tableware. The country has a parliamentary form of democracy where elections are held every five years.

A Better Place (song lyrics)

Gentil Misigaro

I've been looking for a better life and a better place
but I realize something is missing
I am always wishing to see the brightness in life,
I need to see the sunshine again,
here I am without joy, without excitement no comfort,
Somebody give me hope of freedom and justice
let me know if I can breathe again,
I am tired of living in this kind of life looking for love, looking
    for hope

Chorus: I wanna find a better place for me
Where there is no more pain, no more sorrow. Oh yeah
Where there is love, justice, unity and peace.

Sometimes I dream of a paradise place
Seeing flowers of all colours in all corners
And walking like a lion in a jungle
Flying like an eagle when the sky is blue, when everything is
    breathing fresh air, peacefully and hopefully that day will
    come

Chorus: I wanna find a better place for me
Where there is no more pain, no more sorrow. Oh yeah
Where there is love, justice, unity and peace.

Bridge: a better place, a nice place and a greater place for us
that's all we need *x2*.

Chorus: I wanna find a better place for me
Where there is no more pain, no more sorrow. Oh yeah
Where there is love, justice, unity and peace.

Console Mutabazi

Gentil Misigaro is a musician, songwriter, multi-instrumentalist, music producer and music teacher. Born in Congo, he grew up in Rwanda and Uganda in a family of 12, arriving in Canada in 2010.

As a musician, Gentil has performed to small and big audiences including to a crowd of 14,000 people at the MTS Centre in Winnipeg. He has worked on various musical projects as a producer, producing hundreds of songs for other artists from different countries including award-winning performers from Rwanda and Sudan.

Gentil holds a diploma in Music from the Reformed Theological College in Uganda. He is a music instructor at Status4, a community driven non-profit organization that uses music and media arts to provide inspiration, information and opportunity to inner city youth. He is also the founder of *A Better World Movement Inc.*, working to restore peace and building unity through the power of music and stories.

The Democratic Republic of the Congo (French: *République démocratique du Congo*), sometimes referred to as DR Congo, Congo-Kinshasa or the DRC, is a country located in central Africa. It is the second largest country in Africa by area and the eleventh largest in the world. With a population of over 75 million, the Democratic Republic of the Congo is the nineteenth most populous nation in the world, the fourth most populous nation in Africa, as well as the most populous officially Francophone country.

Note to Instructors

We're sure you will enjoy introducing these wonderful stories to your students. It is our hope that the stories will enrich their lives and offer them entertaining and meaningful ways to practise their language skills.

The activities that accompany the stories are designed for adult English as an Additional Language (EAL) learners with a Canadian Language Benchmark (CLB) of 5+. Many activities can be used with a class; however, they can also be used by students who would like to work on their own. There is a range of activities, including discussion questions, vocabulary-building exercises, reading comprehension questions, writing tasks, and even listening exercises. The types of activities vary, so not every story will have the same kind of activities. Consideration has also been given ot the reading process; for this reason, there are pre-, while-, and post-reading activities.

The story grid provides an overview of the CLB reading levels of the stories and the type of vocabulary found in each story. Please note that the CLB levels are approximations. While these stories were not written for a particular reading level, the assigned levels can serve as guidelines in choosing stories that are appropriate for your students.

While the activities have been developed to reinforce the stages of pre-, while-, and post-reading, you may find that it is sometimes necessary to provide some scaffolding activities for your students prior to having them work on their own.

Story Grid

	Story	Approximate Reading Level	Vocabulary
1	*A Place Called Home* Lucy Kaikai	CLB 7+	Thicket, sumptuous, notoriety, nostalgia, vanquish, multitask, indescribable, cherish, recover
2	*The Farewell* Briana Jeon	CLB 5+	Nonsense, farewell, awkward, scolding, cuddles, vacant, graduating
3	*Winnipeg* Julia Kim	CLB 5+	Curiosity, realized, regret, creative, adapted, unique, hyper, flashy, cozy, focus, watercolor
4	*Transit Drivers* Souada Bauer	CLB 6+	Ambassadors, interpretation, vague, vibes, fabricate, destination, suffice, retrieve, maneuvering
5	*Window of Dreams* Jamie Morales	CLB 6+	Abroad, landscape, naive, entrepreneurship, juggle, embraces, hectic, exquisite, striving, misconception
6	*My Love, My Hero* Jay Sagin	CLB 5+	Painkiller, concerned, movements, transferred, umbilical cord, expenses, responsibly, convince
7	*El Dorado* Nina Singh	CLB 7+	Exotic, replicas, lingered, incessant, decipher, genocide, bartering, detached, babblers, trickery

Story	Approximate Reading Level	Vocabulary
8	*Canadian Sonata* Sergio Roysen	Language Difficulty CLB 5+ Concept Difficulty CLB 7+	Coordinates, definition, fist, pressure, tremors, explode, inhale, exhale, approaching
9	*True Love* Nancy Repiso	CLB 6+	Limitations, essence, social network, motivated, relationship, conquer, speechless, witness, risks
10	*More than an Immigrant* German Cruz Reyes	CLB 7+	Stereotype, discrimination, tolerance, condescending, connotation, optimistic, vulnerable, probation, manipulative, intrinsic, implicit, legitimize
11	*Spirits of the North* Faisal Islam	CLB 7+	Interspersed, jetty, silhouette, resins, tranquility, backdrop, mimicking, meridian, subarctic, intermittent, celestial, intruded
12	*A Better Place* Gentil Misigaro	CLB 5+	Comfort, justice, sorrow, realize, paradise, jungle

Questions and Activities

A Place Called Home
Lucy Kaikai

Before Reading

1. In her story, Lucy describes some vivid memories of her home. What memories do you have of your home?
2. What things/people do you think Lucy will mention that she misses from her homeland?
3. Lucy talks about "the home Beyond the Blue". What do you think this expression means?
4. Lucy is from Africa. What foods do you think she talks about?

When you read, you will find the answers to the last three questions, and you can see if your predictions were correct.

Vocabulary

A. Lucy uses very descriptive language in her story. As you read, find the phrases that she uses to express the following ideas.

1. Where she lives, there are different views on what is beautiful.
2. She ate all different kinds of seafood.
3. She felt like a visible minority in her new country.
4. Her name is not remembered in her homeland.
5. She enjoyed singing everywhere.
6. Everyone made eye contact with her.

7. Her hope lies in heaven.

8. There will be world-wide peace.

9. There will no longer be racial discrimination.

10. She ate natural, healthy food.

B. Use the vocabulary below, which is taken from Lucy's story, to fill in the blanks in the following sentences. **You may have to change the form of some of the words to fit the sentence they are in.**

Find the word in the story first, and see if you can guess the meaning from the sentence it is in.

If you cannot guess the meaning, use a dictionary to help you understand the word.

dimples embrace hoarse mansion multitask nostalgia
notoriety pebbles sumptuous thicket

1. The rabbit ran into a _____when it was chased by a fox.

2. My voice is _____ this morning because I was cheering loudly at the basketball game last night.

3. He _____his wife as he welcomed her home after a long trip.

4. The cute little girl had big _____in her cheeks.

5. It's hard to walk barefoot on this beach because it is covered with _____.

6. A feeling of _____came over me when I returned to my country after ten years.

7. The rich man lived in a huge _____with twenty rooms and five servants.

8. Many employees feel overworked because they are expected to _____.

9. The cook prepared a _____meal for the guests at the five-star hotel.

10. The _____ of the criminal had spread because his picture was in every major newspaper in the country.

After Reading

A. Discussion Groups

Discuss the following questions with the people in your group.

1. What is one of your favourite childhood memories?
2. What things are valued more in your culture than they are in Canada?
3. What things are valued more in Canada than they are in your culture?
4. What are some foods that you miss? Is it possible to buy these foods here in Canada?
5. Lucy wishes for peace and equality. What do you wish for?

B. Lucy tells about listening to her grandmother spin tales. Write or make a presentation about a tale that was told to you by someone in your family when you were a child.

The Farewell

by Briana Jeon

Before Reading

1. Can you remember how you felt when you left your country to come to Canada?
2. How old were you when you came here?
3. Briana Jeon was young when she left her country. What do you think that she missed?

A. Reading

1. Who or what is "the best singer"?
2. What clues tell you that Briana is just a young girl?

3. Did Briana's family travel together to Canada?

4. What concerns did Briana have about her grandparents?

5. Briana put on a fake smile twice in her story. When did this happen?

Find the lines in the story that mean the same as the following statements.

1. Briana didn't want to get out of bed right away.

2. Briana was not eager to leave her country.

3. She accepted the fact that she had to say good-bye to her boyfriend.

4. Briana and her father felt uncomfortable on the ride home.

5. Briana's grandmother is suffering from memory loss.

6. Briana was very upset when she saw her grandparents for the last time.

7. In the end, she thinks positively about moving to Canada.

B. Vocabulary

Find *synonyms* (words with similar meanings) in the story for the following words and phrases.

1. Cuddles   2. Empty   3. Graduating high school   4. Ran

Word Families

Fill in the chart with the missing words. If there is an x, that particular word form does not exist.

	Noun	Verb	Adjective	Adverb
1	_____	_____	_____	repeatedly
2	_____	x	awkward	_____
3	distance	_____	_____	_____
4	_____	_____	empty	x
5	_____	_____	comfortable	_____
6	_____	_____	vacant	_____

Check your answers and use the words from the chart to fill in the blanks in the following sentences.

1. After _____ tries, she finally passed her driving test.

   His mother asked him _____ to finish his homework.

   Do you want me to _____ the instructions?

   _____ is important in pronunciation practice.

2. There was an _____ silence between the young man and woman on their first date.

   They were both embarrassed by the _____ of the situation.

   The new teacher smiled _____ at her students on the first day of classes.

3. He had to travel a long _____ to visit his parents.

   She is a _____ relative of mine.

   We are _____ related.

   He has _____ himself from his family; he never sees his parents or his siblings.

4. When Briana knew that she was leaving Korea, she felt an _____ inside her.

   He _____ the recycling bin before the garbage was collected.

   The waiter filled our _____ water glasses.

5. The patient was resting _____ when the doctor came to check on her.

   You can watch movies in the _____ of your home if you have the movie channel.

   I tried to _____ my friend, but I could not make her feel better.

Are you _____ in that chair, or would you like to sit in this one?

6. There are no _____ in that apartment block.

He stared _____ into space during the boring lecture.

You can study in this room; it's _____ until one o'clock.

The students had to _____ the school during the fire drill.

After Reading

Discussion Groups

1. If you have children, tell how they reacted to moving to Canada.

2. What concerns do children have about moving to another country?

3. In what ways are children's concerns the same as adults' concerns?

4. In what ways are they different?

Writing

1. In her story, Briana describes what it was like to say good-bye to her grandparents.

   Write a paragraph about what it was like to say good-bye to someone in your country before you came here.

2. Write a paragraph giving advice to parents about helping their children to accept the idea of moving to another country.

Winnipeg
by Julia Kim

Before Reading

1. When did you arrive in Winnipeg?
2. Did all of your family members arrive at the same time?
3. Julia Kim arrived in Winnipeg in January. What do you think her first impressions of Winnipeg were?

A. Reading

1. Which member of the Kim family did not arrive in Winnipeg on January 23?
2. Why did Julia and her daughters have to shorten their winter walk?
3. What happened after Julia and her daughters left the St. Vital Mall?
4. Who finally helped them?
5. What does Julia's daughter enjoy doing?
6. Now that the Kims are used to the winter, what do they enjoy doing?
7. What in particular does Julia like about the libraries here?
8. What two sports do Julia and her daughters enjoy in the summer?
9. What adjectives does Julia use to describe Winnipeg?
10. What does Julia mean when she says that Winnipeg is coming close to her heart?

True or False? Put T for true or F for false in front of each statement.

___ 1. Julia came to Winnipeg alone.

___ 2. Julia and her daughters went for a nice, long walk in the winter.

___ 3. Julia and her daughters visited the St. Vital Mall soon after they arrived in Winnipeg.

   4.   A police officer had to drive them home from the mall.

   5.   Julia's daughters have adapted to winter in Winnipeg.

B. Vocabulary

Scrambled Words: Unscramble the words in the following sentences.

1. When I went out in the cold, my feet felt **nozerf**.
2. I like to put lots of **sharmlowmals** in my hot chocolate.
3. It's fun to throw **sobwallns** in the winter.
4. I love going to the **barryil** to pick out books.
5. He lives in a big **patartmen** block downtown.

Adjectives: Find the adjectives that Julia uses to describe the following nouns.

1. Apartments:_____
2. Winnipeg:_____
3. Villages: _____
4. Brands: _____
5. How she feels in Winnipeg: _____

Comparisons

In her story, Julia uses a lot of comparisons (similes). Find the words that she uses to compare the following words.

1. The cold air entered the house like _____.
2. The clouds were sweet and soft like _____.
3. Winnipeg's sunny sky seems to resemble _____.
4. The sky tells a story with clouds like _____.
5. Julia plays with her daughters like _____.

Make some of your own comparisons for the following words.

Note: There is no answer key for this exercise.

1. She crept into the room like _____.
2. The hungry boy ate his lunch like _____.

3. The bright sun resembles _____.

4. The snow was falling like _____.

5. The loud noise sounded like _____.

After Reading

Discussion Groups

1. What are some things that you enjoy doing in Winnipeg in the summer and in the winter?

2. Julia talks about going to a park with her daughters. Tell about a park that you have visited here.
   What did you do at the park?

3. At the end of the story, Julia tells what she likes about Winnipeg and how she feels here. What do you like about Winnipeg? What three adjectives describe how you feel here?

4. Do you agree that Winnipeg is quiet, beautiful, and small? What three adjectives would you use to describe Winnipeg?

Writing

1. Describe what either winter or summer is like in your hometown. How is it different from winter or summer in Winnipeg?

2. Tell which is your favourite season in Winnipeg and explain why.

Transit Drivers

by Souada Bauer

Before Reading

1. Do you use the bus often?

2. What do you think of the bus drivers here?

3. From her experience using the bus, the author has divided Winnipeg bus drivers into four types.

What do you think those four types could be?

A. Reading

1. What does the expression ambassador "to be" mean?
2. What are the adjectives that Souada uses to describe each of the four types of bus drivers?
3. What surprises Souada about the bus driver who reminds people about where to get off the bus?
4. What does the "security" type of bus driver check carefully?
5. What is meant by a "power hour limit"?
6. Why was Souada going to the College de St. Boniface?

B. Vocabulary

Matching Match each word or expression on the left with its meaning.

_____ 1. vague   A. scary

_____ 2. to vent   B. to make up

_____ 3. homegrown   C. uncommon

_____ 4. rare   D. not clear

_____ 5. heart stopping E. place where you want to go

_____ 6. to fabricate   F. to rant

_____ 7. destination   G. local

Fill in the blanks by using the seven words and expressions from the left-hand column of the exercise above.

1. I prefer to buy _____ vegetables from Manitoba farmers.
2. When I'm upset, I often _____ to my friends.
3. I don't believe him because he often _____ stories.
4. We arrived at our final _____ late last night.

5. Warm days are _____ in Winnipeg in January.

6. I had a(n) _____ experience the first time I tried down-hill skiing.

7. I wasn't paying attention, so I had only a(n) _____ idea of what the teacher was talking about.

Complete each phrase in the left column with the correct word in the right column.

_____ 1. To hand someone   A. a bus pass

_____ 2. To vent   B. life

_____ 3. To scrutinize   C. a dormant language

_____ 4. To awaken   D. frustration

_____ 5. To reflect on   E. a transfer

Idioms and Expressions

Fill in the words missing from the idioms and expressions in the sentences below. You will find all these idioms/expressions in the story.

1. How on _____ do bus drivers remain so patient?

2. When I have nothing to say, I _____up.

3. His _____eyes noticed everything.

4. I thought I'd lost my wallet, but lo and _____, I found it in my coat pocket!

5. He drove fast because he was on a _____to get to his class on time.

After Reading

Discussion Groups

In small groups, discuss the following questions.

1. Have you ever had bus drivers like the ones described by Souada? Which ones have you encountered? If not, describe the kinds of drivers you have had.

2. Souada tells her story with a lot of humour. What parts of the story made you laugh?

3. What differences are there between taking the bus in Winnipeg and taking the bus in your home town?

Writing Write a paragraph on any or all of the following topics.

1. Compare taking the bus in your home town to taking the bus in Winnipeg.

2. Describe a memorable experience that you had when you were taking the bus in Winnipeg or in your home town.

3. In your opinion, what are the characteristics of the ideal bus driver?

Window of Dreams

by Jamie Morales

Before Reading

1. Jamie reflects on what she has gained in coming to Canada. What do you think she will mention?

2. She talks about living on the prairies. What things about the prairies (or Manitoba) were striking to you? When you read, see if Jamie mentions the same points.

3. She also writes about the challenges of being an immigrant. What challenges do you think she will talk about?

A. Reading Put T for true or F for false in front of each of the following statements.

___ 1. Jamie was on the "pro" side of the debate in her classroom.

___ 2. The decision to come to Canada was not made by the whole family.

___ 3. Jamie has no brothers or sisters.

___ 4. Jamie always knew that she would attend university some day.

___ 5. Jamie studies with other students from abroad.

___ 6. Jamie is still a teenager.

___ 7. Jamie has found that immigrants have made sacrifices to live in Canada.

___ 8. Jamie's father is a factory worker.

___ 9. Jamie finds that all the people in Canada have everything they need.

___ 10. Jamie has some regrets about her relatives back home.

___ 11. The bond between her and some of her relatives has weakened.

___ 12. Jamie feels that it is always wise to pay attention to the advice of others.

Answer the following questions.

1. How old is Jamie now (use the clues in the story to calculate her age).

2. Why do you think she called her story "Window of Dreams"?

3. What indicates to you that Jamie is probably a very good student?

4. What support does Jamie use to show that her mother has made sacrifices?

5. Why does Jamie think that she has to have a car?

6. What has caused Jamie to lose touch with some relatives?

7. Why could Jamie not afford to buy a $1.25 drink at school at one time?

8. When Jamie says "I have no regrets" what does she mean?

B. Vocabulary

Find the words in the story that mean the same as the following words.

1. protected
2. staring at
3. enthusiastic
4. without worries
5. the best grades
6. hugs
7. putting together
8. relatives
9. ties between people
10. careful with money

Jamie uses some great expressions in her writing. Here are a few of them.

- to be a bowl of cherries
- to make ends meet
- time flies
- to juggle jobs
- to flip burgers

Find these expressions in Jamie's story and see how they are used. Now, use them in the sentences below, using the context to help you make your choice. You may have to change the form of the verb in some expressions to fit into the sentences.

1. Many teenagers get their first job _____ at a fast-food restaurant.

2. _____ isn't easy. You have to run from one part-time job to the next one.

3. When you enjoy your work, you find that _____ while you're at work.

4. Many immigrants have to work at two low-paying jobs just to _____.

5. We all have our struggles in life, and we learn that life is not always_____.

After Reading

Discussion Groups

1. Jamie describes her parents' struggles since immigrating to Canada. What other struggles do immigrants face?
2. What benefits do immigrants gain?
3. What advice would you give to a friend or a relative who is thinking of immigrating here?
4. Jamie talks a lot about her dreams. What dream(s) did you have when you were young? What dreams do you have now?
5. Jamie talks about some of the experiences she has had here. Share an experience that you have had.

Writing

Write about your thoughts on immigrating to Canada. What made you decide to come to Canada?

How do you feel about your decision now that you are here?

My Love, My Hero

Jay Sagin

Before Reading

1. If you have children, what do you remember about their birth?
2. If you are a male, were you there to see your children being born?
3. This story is written by a man who was there for the birth of his child. What kind of support do you think that he could give his wife during the birth of their baby?

A. Reading Read the following statements about the story and decide if they are true or false. Put T for true or F for false in front of each statement.

_____ 1. Jay's wife could have taken painkillers while she was giving birth to the baby.

_____ 2. Jay's wife was very concerned about the baby.

_____ 3. Jay was allowed to be present only while the baby was being born.

_____ 4. Jay wished he could share the pain his wife was feeling.

_____ 5. Jay and his wife had prepared for the birth of their baby.

B. Vocabulary

Find the words in the story that have the same or similar meanings to the following words.

1. Give birth
2. To be worried
3. Medication to help ease the pain
4. Instructed
5. To protect

Word Families

Fill in the chart with the missing word forms. If there is an *x*, that particular word form does not exist.

	Noun	Verb	Adjective	Adverb
1	pain/painkiller	_____	_____	_____
2	movement	_____	_____	x
3	expenses	x	_____	_____
4	creation	_____	_____	_____
5	concern	_____	_____	x

Now, check your answers, and use the various words from the chart to fill in the blanks below.

1. 1. He took a _____ because he had a _____ in his chest.

   It _____ me to read about wars in our world.

   The poor young man was _____ shy.

2. The baby started to _____ , and I felt the _____ as I placed my hand on my wife's belly.

   I was _____ by the kindness that the stranger showed to me.

3. He dresses_____ ! Did you see that _____ suit that he's wearing?

   They watched their _____ carefully as they saved to buy a house.

4. That artist has _____ a masterpiece.

   He is taking a _____ writing course this year.

   She answered the questions very _____ !

5. The doctor was _____ about his patient's health.

   I have a _____ about my grade on this exam.

   Please don't ask me any questions; this matter doesn't _____ you.

After Reading

A. Discussion Groups

In a group, discuss these questions with your classmates.

1. Do you think Jay will be a good father? What makes you feel that way?

2. Parents should prepare in many ways for the birth of a child. Discuss some ways of preparing.

3. In your country, do fathers watch or help during the birth of their children? If so, has this always been the case?

4. Is it more common in your country for babies to be born at home or in the hospital?

5. What are some of the hopes and dreams that parents have for their children?

B. Writing

The birth of a child is certainly a memorable experience for parents. Write a paragraph about an experience in your life that was memorable. Be sure to add a lot of details.

El Dorado

by Nina Singh

Before Reading

1. In this story, the author writes a tale about an imaginary place. Does your culture have any tales about imaginary places?

2. Have you ever been to a place that was very different from what you had expected it to be?

3. Have you ever heard of the city of El Dorado? What do you know about it?

A. Reading

Find the lines in the story that indicate the following.

1. The ruler of the Golden City was well liked.

2. The little girl's eyes were different from her mother's eyes.

3. The girl's eyes were blue.

4. The girl wanted to visit the Golden City.

5. The tower where the girl's family lived was crowded.

6. Some of the people in the tower began to communicate with each other.

7. Women went searching for their lost husbands.

8. The girl regrets her decision to come to "that place."

What is meant by the following phrases, or what is the author making a reference to?

1. The Golden City glittered like an undiscovered jewel.

2. I only heard what I wanted to hear.

3. They needed us ....to do their dirty work.

4. Ghosts of the people turned to dust in Nagasaki.

5. That place where they let you freeze if you do not have exact change.

B. Vocabulary

Match each word on the right with its meaning or synonym on the left.

_____ 1. incessant babbling   A. trickery

_____ 2. precious gifts   B. awful truth

_____ 3. horrifying reality   C. shine

_____ 4. dirty work   D. difficult job that no one wants to do

_____ 5. barter   E. constant talking

_____ 6. motherland   F. promise

_____ 7. deception   G. figure out, understand

_____ 8. exploit   H. valuable presents

_____ 9. vow   I. home country

_____10. glitter   J. protect

_____11. shield   K. take advantage for personal gain

_____12. decipher   L. trade for goods rather than for money

Adjectives

Nina uses many adjectives to make her writing more vivid. Fill in the blanks with the missing adjectives from her story.

1. The people who lived in the Golden City ate the _____ foods.

2. Their houses were _____ red.

3. The girl's mother had the eyes of a(n) _____ empress.

4. The Golden City shone like a(n) _____ jewel.

5. The kingdom where the girl lived had a(n) _____ tower.

6. In the girl's kingdom, her family members loved each other despite their _____ babbling.

7. The Golden City was a(n) _____ kingdom.

8. The girl's mother tried to protect her from the _____ reality.

9. Those people in the Golden City needed others to do their _____ work.

10. The ghosts of _____ souls haunted the land below the tower.

11. Among the many ghosts were the ghosts of people who had died in the _____ sea of discovering a better life.

12. The tower was described as a(n) _____ concoction.

13. The people in the tower missed the ways of their _____ motherland.

14. The mothers didn't want to see their babies, so they stayed in a _____ room in the tower.

15. The _____ tower was home to
    _____babblers.

16. The women whose husbands had left searched for a(n)
    _____ face by the ocean's edge.

17. The belongings of the exploited people are displayed in
    _____ buildings.

18. The doctor must examine you to ensure that your body is
    neither _____ nor _____.

19. She wishes she hadn't continued her _____
    daydreaming.

20. She should have paid attention to the _____
    story that her mother had tried to tell her.

Using Prepositions

Fill in the blanks with the correct prepositions. Note that some
have to be used more than once.

Prepositions: *of* (5 times), *off in for from* (twice), *on out* (twice),
to with

1. The family members were different, owing _____ their
   different experiences.

2. They loved each other in spite _____ these differences.

3. They used to live _____ the land by growing their own
   vegetables.

4. There were ghosts _____ the murdered and condemned
   in the tower.

5. There were also ghosts _____ the Middle East.

6. The tower had the outline _____ a dying man.

7. The cripples called _____ _____agony.

8. Some people began to barter _____necessities.

9. The people held _____to the memory of their homeland.

10. The women were detached _____those around them.

11. In that place, they knew nothing ____dying.

12. They welcomed us _____open arms.

13. Her heart was ripped _____ ____ her chest.

After Reading

Discussion Groups

1. Tell about the expectations that you had when you first came here.

2. Now that you are here, which of your expectations were met, and which ones were not?

3. In your group, discuss the meaning of the description of "that place". For example, what is the author referring to when she says that the following things happen in "that place"?

   · They display our belongings in gilded buildings as if they were theirs.

   · Nothing is given without a price.

   · Their elderly die alone because they are no longer useful.

   · You bleed every day from stepping on the sharp, shattered pieces of your former self.

   · You are welcomed with open arms, as long as you know your place.

4. Some historic events are discussed in the paragraph about the ghosts. What is the significance of the following ghosts?

   · ghosts from the "dark" continent

   · ghosts of the Chinese railway workers

   · ghosts of the people turned to dust in Nagasaki

   · ghosts of those who were here first, who will never forget the pain of their calculated genocide

Writing

1. Do some research on the fabled city of El Dorado and write about what you discover.
2. What would you tell people who plan to come to your hometown so that they will know what to expect? You can focus on the weather, the customs, or any other aspect that you think people should know about. Pick just one aspect.
3. What do you think is the most important thing that people coming to Winnipeg should know about, and why?

Canadian Sonata
by Sergio Roysen

Before Reading

1. What do you remember about arriving in Canada?
2. How did you feel at that time?

Reading

Answer the following questions about Sergio's poem.

1. What does Sergio mean when he uses these words: "Home. The Map. Easy definition Impossible task"?
2. Why do you think he uses the chest, the right side of the brain, and fists to describe the coordinates on a map?
3. In the part of the poem called "Rules", Sergio uses these words: "it's absent", "it doesn't exist", and "it's not yours". What do you think "it" is?
4. In the parts of the poem that start with the words "Feel" and "Create", Sergio describes some things that are impossible to do. What are they?
5. In the last part of the poem ("Fight"), Sergio says "it's worth it". What do you think he is referring to?.
6. In the last part of the poem, Sergio says, "Shake the tremors off your shoulders and advance." What do you think he means?

After Reading

A. Discussion Groups

Talk in your group about the poem and share what parts you like and what they mean to you.

B.

Write your own poem expressing your thoughts about leaving your country to live in a different place.

True Love

by Nancy Repiso

Before Reading

1. Do you believe that there is a specific person for each of us who is meant to be our partner in life?
2. What do you think of long distance romances?
3. Do you know anyone who has started a romantic relationship with someone on Facebook?

A. Reading Put T in front of the statements that are true and F in front of those that are false.

_____ 1. Nancy arrived in Winnipeg on Christmas day.

_____ 2. In the end, she was determined to find a partner who was good-looking, rich, professional, and intelligent.

_____ 3. After a while, she changed her mind about the type of man she hoped to meet.

_____ 4. Nancy's childhood friend invited her on Facebook.

_____ 5. Nancy was not in Japan when the tsunami and earth-quake struck.

_____ 6. Nancy prayed a special prayer for a few days.

_____ 7. At first, she had her doubts that the long distance relationship with Edwin could be successful.

_____ 8. Because theirs is a long distance relationship, Nancy and Edwin have never experienced any problems.

_____ 9. Nancy received the special letter from Edwin in time for their "anniversary".

_____ 10. Edwin proposed to Nancy in the letter.

_____ 11. Nancy and Edwin will be married in Canada.

_____ 12. They will have guests at their wedding ceremony.

Find the lines in the story that give the following information.

1. Nancy became a better person as a result of living away from home.

2. She realized that her life was incomplete without a partner.

3. The characteristics of a partner that she had originally thought were important were not really very important.

4. Nancy and Edwin talked about more than just the good things that were happening in their lives.

5. Nancy wasn't positive that their long term relationship could last.

6. Edwin proposed to Nancy through social media.

7. Nancy plans to have a religious marriage ceremony.

Matching

Complete each phrase from the story by matching the start of the phrase on the left with the correct ending on the right.

_____ 1. To be sensitive	A. of getting something
_____ 2. To have limitations	B. for someone
_____ 3. To prepare/ condition yourself	C. in a relationship
_____ 4. To know	D. to others' emotions
_____ 5. A person who is meant	E. in your heart
_____ 6. To work	F. of my life
_____ 7. To pray	G. in someone

_____8. To see yourself H. as a welder

_____9. To be I. as a person

_____10. To lose hope J. for me

_____11. The happiest day K. for a wedding

_____12. To plan L. for an awaited moment

B. Vocabulary

Use the following words from the story in the blanks in the sentences.

condition conquer foundation long distance perception relationship risk sensitive social network value

1. When you care about how other people feel, you are _____ to them.

2. When you know someone well, you can establish a (n) _____ with that person.

3. To be ready for a big race, you have to _____ yourself for it.

4. The way you see or view things is your _____ of things.

5. Facebook is an example of a(n)_____ _____.

6. When you really care about what another person thinks, you _____ that person's opinion.

7. Two people who live in two different countries can develop a(n)_____ relationship.

8. A serious relationship should be based on a strong _____.

9. If you are determined, you can often _____ your fears.

10. Sometimes you have to take a(n) _____, even if you're not sure you will succeed.

Word Families

Fill in the chart with the missing word forms. If there is an x, that particular word form does not exist.

	Noun	Verb	Adjective	Adverb
1	_____	x	_____	emotionally
2	_____	_____	sensitive	_____
3	_____	to value/devalue	_____	_____
4	risk	_____	_____	x
5	relationship	_____	_____	x

Now, check your answers, and use the various words from the chart to fill in the blanks below.

1. He couldn't hide his _____when he found out that he had won the contest.

   It was such an _____experience for him.

   He spoke _____of his love for his family.

2. The _____little girl cried when her friend teased her.

   Everyone was aware of the _____of the situation. They knew that the matter had to be handled

   _____.

   Parents must _____their children to the feelings of others.

3. I _____you as a friend.

   Their currency has recently been

   _____.

   He has made a _____contribution to the team this year.

4. I don't want to _____ losing my money in that scheme.

Many people avoid gambling because they don't want to take _____ with their money.

Skiing down that high mountain looks too _____ for me.

5. She and her parents have a wonderful

_____.

You two must be _____ ; you look so much alike.

That teacher _____ very well to her students.

Missing Words

Fill in the blanks with the missing words. The number after some of the words indicates how many times those words will be used.

as (2) in (3) of (2) for (4) to

1. Teachers should be sensitive _____ their students' feelings.
2. He has his limitations _____ a writer.
3. I prepared myself _____ the long journey.
4. He knew _____ his heart that he didn't really love her.
5. The bride and groom were truly meant _____ each other.
6. In her country, she had worked _____ a nurse.
7. We prayed _____ our friend who was in the hospital.
8. I often see myself _____ my children.
9. He was _____ a relationship with a wonderful woman.
10. The ship-wrecked sailors lost hope _____ reaching the shore.
11. The day I graduated from university was one of the happiest days _____ my life.

12. We are planning _____ our retirement now by saving money.

After Reading

Group Discussions

1. In your opinion, what are the challenges of a long distance relationship?
2. If you have had a long distance relationship, share your thoughts about it with the others in your group.
3. Edwin had an unusual way of proposing marriage to Nancy. Share any other unusual ways of proposing that you have heard about.
4. If you are married, tell how your partner proposed to you.

A Debate

Have an informal debate with the people in your group. Divide your group into two.

- One group will argue that Facebook is a good place to meet potential partners.
- The other group will argue that Facebook is not a good place for meeting potential partners.
- Each group should make as many points as possible to support their opinion.

Writing

Edwin says that Nancy has all the characteristics that he is looking for in a wife. Describe the characteristics that are important to you in a partner or a friend and explain why these characteristics are important.

More than an Immigrant: the remaking of self within a culture of silence
by German Cruz Reyes

Before Reading

1. Have you changed since coming to Canada? Have your feelings about being here changed?

2. The author relates both positive and negative experiences he has had since coming here. What positive and negative experiences have you had? As you read, see if your experiences are similar to German's experiences.

3. How long do you think it takes to adapt to a new culture/ country?

4. In your opinion, what factors determine how well a person will adapt?

A. Reading

1. Why does German say that he was naive when he first came to Canada?

2. What is one concern that he still has?

3. In which two ways did people condescend to German when they spoke to him?

4. Why did German feel that he had to learn English quickly?

5. What made German's warehouse job so stressful?

6. Why didn't he quit his job?

7. What made him feel "angry, humiliated, abused and exploited"?

8. What did German find out later about the company he had been working for?

9. Where has German experienced what he calls a "culture of silence"?

10. What is stressful about the type of racism that German has observed?
11. How does segregation occur, according to German?
12. What does German recommend that we do to have a positive cultural experience?
13. What impressed him when he came to Winnipeg?
14. What happened to him when he went back to Mexico?
15. What happens to "the puzzle" when people immigrate to another country?
16. According to German, what do immigrants have to realize and accept?
17. What do we have no control over and what can we choose in our lives?

Find the following lines in German's story and explain what he means when he makes these statements.

1. "No big deal everything is the same no matter where you live."
2. "My worries of living here...took me out of my comfort zone."
3. "I could feel it in the energy."
4. "It was the most vulnerable time in my life."
5. "Racism is hiding within the culture of silence."
6. "When you move to another country, the puzzle that you relatively had together, is now all over the place."
7. "We make Canada and Canada makes us."

B. Vocabulary

Matching Match each word on the left with its opposite on the right.

_____ 1. tolerance   A. superiority

_____ 2. awkward   B. valued

_____ 3. rude   C. pessimistic

_____ 4. vulnerable   D. discrimination

_____ 5. exploited   E. comfortable

_____ 6. unconscious   F. polite

_____ 7. inferiority   G. included

_____ 8. harmony   H. confident

_____ 9. isolated   I. aware

_____ 10. optimistic   J. discord

Matching Complete each phrase contained in German's story by putting the two parts of the phrase together.

_____ 1. culture   A. correct

_____ 2. cultural   B. english

_____ 3. comfort   C. attitude

_____ 4. forced   D. rich

_____ 5. limited   E. nature

_____ 6. optimistic   F. identity

_____ 7. work   G. zone

_____ 8. manipulative   H. clashes

_____ 9. politically   I. smile

_____ 10. physical   J. culture

_____ 11. mentally   K. system

_____ 12. human   L. complex

_____ 13. inferiority   M. environment

_____ 14. dominant   N. violence

_____ 15. culturally   O. stressful

Check your answers, then use the phases that you have made in order to complete the following exercise.

Note: Not all 15 phrases will be used.

1. Because of his _____, the immigrant to Canada had trouble expressing himself well.

2. I was out of my _____ in that awkward situation.

3. Usually, I have a(n) _____, but today I'm feeling rather negative.

4. In Canada, we are expected to be as _____ as possible.

5. It is very difficult to do your job well in a hostile _____ _____.

6. I wasn't feeling happy, but I had to put on a(n) _____ _____ in front of my friends.

7. People who act superior can give others a(n) _____.

8. We sometimes feel jealous of others; it's just _____ to feel that way.

9. Peace-loving people try to avoid _____.

10. Unfortunately, in a multicultural society, _____ sometimes occur.

11. Which is the _____ in this country?

12. A country that is made up of people from many different cultures is certainly _____.

Word Groups

- Look in German's story to find words that have the following **suffixes** (word endings attached to the root word). You may want to work in groups, assigning two or three suffixes to each group.
- The number after each suffix indicates the number of words you should be able to find for each suffix.
- When you have found the words, look at them and see if they are nouns, verbs, adjectives, or adverbs. See if there are any exceptions, or if there are words that can be used in more than one way.

Note: Some of the nouns may be plural in the story. In that case, just write them in their singular forms on your list.

1. -ance/-ence (6)   2. -ant/-ent (4)   3. -tion (14)   4. -ive (4)
5. -able (4)   6. -ity (8)   7. -ment (4)   8. -al (6)   9. -ful (3)
10. -ic (2)

Check the answers in the answer key. Use words from each numbered set of words to fill in the blanks in the following exercise.

1. **-ance/-ence**

    There is a great _____ between his
    _____ and yours because he has
    had many different _____ in his life.

2. **-ant/-ent**

    The life of a(n) _____ is often quite
    _____ from the life
    of those who belong to the _____ culture.

3. **-tion**

    Did he _____ that he has experienced
    _____, _____, and
    _____ ?

4. **-ive**

    He works with a(n) _____ and
    _____ boss. He feels so unhappy!

5. **-able**

    It's _____ that he feels so
    _____ , _____, and
    _____ in his workplace.

6. **-ity**

    The _____ of the situation is there is no
    _____ for him to be promoted in
    his workplace. As a result, he has developed feelings of
    _____.

7. **-ment**

In his _____ to his employees, the manager expressed his _____ about their lack of concern for the _____ .

8. **-al**

In a(n) _____ country, can people retain their _____identity?

9. **-ful**

His life with his _____ wife was far from _____ ; in fact, it was very _____ because he could never make her happy.

10. **-ic**

He had a(n) _____ desire to be _____ in life.

After Reading

Discussion Groups

1. Did you live in a multicultural country before coming to Canada? Share some of the challenges or benefits of living in a multicultural society.

2. Can you relate to the experiences that German has had here? Share some of the experiences (both good and bad) that you have had as an immigrant.

3. Give your opinions of German's thoughts about adapting and changing. How have you changed since you came here?

Writing

1. Adapting to a new culture is a process that takes time. Do some research on the steps involved in the process and summarize them. Conclude by telling what stage you believe that you are at in the process and why you think you are at that stage.

2. German realized when he went back to Mexico that he was no longer completely comfortable in his homeland. Do you think it would be easy for you to re-adapt to your home country? What would you find it hard to re-adapt to?

3. What advice would you give to someone planning to immigrate to Canada in order to make it easier for that person to adapt to living here?

Spirits of the North
by Faisal Islam

Pre-Reading

1. When you came to Canada, was there anything that you had heard about that you really wanted to see?
2. What do you know about northern Canada?
3. Faisal had the opportunity to go to northern Canada. What do you think he wanted to see?
4. What sorts of things do you think he saw on his trip? How do you think he traveled during his trip?
5. Someone showed Faisal the sights when he was on his trip. Who do you think that person was?

You can verify your guesses for #3, 4, and 5 when you read the story.

Reading

Answer the following questions.

1. Why did Faisal take a canoe trip at night?
2. What kinds of wood were used to make the canoe?
3. In his story, Faisal talks about "the more distant performers." Who or what are they?
4. What are the clues that Fred is probably Aboriginal?
5. Why do you think that Faisal refers to this spot as "this sacred place"?

A. Vocabulary

Faisal uses some excellent vocabulary in his story to describe what he sees on his trip.

Try matching the vocabulary on the left with the meaning on the right by putting the letter of the meaning in front of each word.

Find the word in the story first, and see if you can guess the meaning from the sentence it is in.

Take the word out of the sentence and replace it with the meaning that you chose, and see if the sentence makes sense.

_____ 1. blanketing   A. far off

_____ 2. camouflaged   B. colors

_____ 3. celestial   C. outline

_____ 4. chanting   D. a place to tie up boats

_____ 5. emerge   E. hidden

_____ 6. gear   F. equipment

_____ 7. grin   G. smile

_____ 8. grandeur   H. destroy

_____ 9. hues   I. constant

___ 10. incessant   J. come out

___ 11. intermittent   K. related to the stars/ superior, outstanding

___ 12. jetty   L. beauty, majesty

___ 13. mariner   M. covering

___ 14. randomly   N. a type of singing

___ 15. remote   O. sailor

___ 16. serpent   P. now and then, not always

___ 17. shatter   Q. related to the sky

___ 18. shimmering   R. with no fixed pattern

___ 19. silhouette   S. snake

___ 20. stellar   T. shining

B. Use the following words in the sentences below. Each word should be used just once.

You may have to change the form of some words to fit the sentence they are in.

blanket   emerge   gear   grin   grandeur   jetty   randomly
remote   shatter   stellar

1. The proud father had a huge _____ on his face when he saw his baby daughter.

2. When we got to the water, we found the boat tied to the _____.

3. We are hoping that the truth will _____ during the trial.

4. The opera star was given a standing ovation for her _____ performance.

5. His dreams of becoming a professional athlete were _____ after his car accident.

6. The snow _____ the ground and made everything white.

7. Everyone is amazed by the _____ of the Rocky Mountains.

8. Do you have all of your _____ ready for our hike in the mountains?

9. The people who took part in the survey were _____ chosen.

10. The people in the _____ village seldom saw people from outside their community.

C. Using two-word verbs.

There are many two-word verbs used in the story. See if you can add the correct preposition after each verb in the following sentences.

away back for in (used twice) **on out** (used twice)
up (used twice)

1. The stars faded _____ as morning approached, and we decided to pack _____ our gear.
2. It was time to load _____ the canoe with our gear and head _____ home.
3. He pointed _____ something in the bushes, but it was too dark for me to make _____ what it was.
4. There was so much beauty to take _____ that I couldn't focus _____ just one thing.
5. I'd like to come _____ next year and book _____ to the same hotel.

After Reading

A

1. Find out more about the northern lights.
   - What causes them?
   - Where and when can they be seen?
   - Are there excursions that you can take to see them?
   - Write or report to your class about what you found out.
2. Read about the myth of Princess Vega and her lover Altair. Write a summary or give an oral summary of this myth.

B. Discussion Groups

In a group, discuss these questions with your classmates.

1. Have you ever seen the northern lights?
2. What spectacles of nature do you have in your country? Describe one.
3. What spectacles of nature have you seen? These spectacles could be in your country, in Canada, or in another country you have visited.
4. Have you ever traveled by canoe? Have you ever used any unusual forms of transportation?

A Better Place
by Gentil Misigaro

Before Reading

In his song, Gentil sings of "a better place". What do you think he hopes to find there?

Reading

Now read the lyrics to the song and answer the following questions.

1. Read the first verse of the song and make a list of all the things Gentil feels are missing from his life.
2. When he has these things, what will they bring back to his life?
3. Gentil makes two comparisons in the second verse of the song. What are they?
4. Which comparison represents a feeling of pride? Which one represents a feeling of freedom?
5. Find the opposites for the following words:

   a. hatred   b. war   c. unfairness   d. sadness   e. despair
   f. happiness

After Reading

A. Discussion Groups

Discuss the following questions with the people in your group.

1. What would you like to see in "a better place"?
2. Write a song with your group, based on Gentil's song, replacing some of the words with your own words. Perform your song to the other groups.

B.

In his song, Gentil makes some comparisons using animals. For example, he says "Walking like a lion in a jungle" and "Flying like an eagle when the sky is blue".

We often use animals in comparisons that are made in this way: *as (adjective) as a(n) animal*

Try matching the correct animal in each comparison below. Put the letter of each animal in the blank in front of each expression.

_____1. As strong as a(n)   A. bat

_____ 2. As sly as a(n)   B. bear

_____ 3. As busy as a(n)   C. bee / beaver

_____ 4. As proud as a(n)   D. bird

_____ 5. As gentle as a(n)   E. clam

_____ 6. As blind as a(n)   F. fox

_____ 7. As graceful as a(n) G. lamb

_____ 8. As happy as a(n)   H. ox

_____ 9. As free as a(n)   I. peacock

____ 10. As grumpy as a(n) J. swan

C. Write down some comparisons to animals that you have in your country and share them with your class. It is interesting to find out what qualities other people give to animals.

ANSWER KEY

A Place Called Home
Lucy Kaikai

Vocabulary
A.
1. "Home is where my plump thighs are called beautiful, not my skinny arms; a gap in your teeth and rings of fat around your neck are as desirable as dimples."
2. "Every creature in the Atlantic ended up in my belly."
3. "...a black dot on a white sheet."
4. "My name sandpapered from the wooden benches where it was once engraved."
5. "My voice was sung hoarse in every church, every school, every stage."
6. "Nobody avoided my eyes."
7. "My hope lies in the home Beyond the Blue."
8. "Wars will cease on every land."
9. "Our colours will fade into one."
10. "Organic foods nourished my fast growing body that was unknown to growth hormones."

B.

1. thicket
2. hoarse
3. embraced
4. dimples
5. pebbles
6. nostalgia
7. mansion
8. multitask
9. sumptuous
10. notoriety

The Farewell
by Briana Jeon

A.

1. "The best singer" is a sparrow/a bird.
2. We know that Briana is just a young girl because of the following:
   - She calls her parents mummy and daddy.
   - She says that she and her boyfriend were too young.
   - After her meeting with her boyfriend her daddy took her home.
   - She likes her father's cuddles.
   - She hasn't graduated from high school yet.
3. No, her father didn't travel to Canada with her family.
4. Briana was concerned about her grandfather's poor health and her grandmother's forgetfulness.

   She was concerned that she would never see them again, and that she would not be at her grandfather's funeral.

5. Briana put on a fake smile when she said good-bye to her boyfriend and after crying about leaving her grandparents.

Find the lines in the story that mean the same as the following statements.

1. Briana didn't want to get out of bed right away.

   "I knew it was time to wake up, but I just rubbed my face repeatedly with the covers. I felt so comfortable and snug, like I was on the clouds."

2. Briana was not eager to leave her country.

   "Ugh, right. Today we are moving."

3. She accepted the fact that she had to say good-bye to her boyfriend.

   "I knew tears couldn't change anything. The past was past."

4. Briana and her father felt uncomfortable on the ride home.

   "My dad and I love each other so much, but there was something awkward between us."

5. Briana's grandmother is suffering from memory loss.

   "She also forgets things easily. Whenever I go to her home, she asks me more than five times whether I ate dinner, although we had dinner together."

6. Briana was very upset when she saw her grandparents for the last time.

   "Today is when I almost cried. If I gathered all the tears that have dropped from my eyes, they would fill a cup."

7. In the end, she thinks positively about moving to Canada.

   "Yes, I think this is a good choice. This is a proper chance, and I think this is going to be good for me."

B. Vocabulary

Synonyms

1. Hugs
2. Vacant
3. Completing my studies
4. Rushed

Word Families

	Noun	Verb	Adjective	Adverb
1	*repetition*	*to repeat*	*repeated*	*repeatedly*
2	*awkwardness*	x	*awkward*	*awkwardly*
3	*distance*	*to distance (oneself)*	*distant*	*distantly*
4	*emptiness*	*to empty*	*empty*	x
5	*comfort*	*to comfort*	*comfortable*	*comfortably*
6	*vacancy*	*to vacate*	*vacant*	*vacantly*

Check your answers and use the words from the chart to fill in the blanks in the following sentences.

1. After repeated tries, she finally passed her driving test.

   His mother asked him repeatedly to finish his homework.

   Do you want me to repeat the instructions?

   Repetition is important in pronunciation practice.

2. There was an awkward silence between the young man and woman on their first date.

   They were both embarrassed by the awkwardness of the situation.

   The new teacher smiled awkwardly at her students on the first day of classes.

3. He had to travel a long distance to visit his parents.

   She is a distant relative of mine.

   We are distantly related.

He has distanced himself from his family; he never sees his parents or his siblings.

4. When Briana knew that she was leaving Korea, she felt an emptiness inside her.

   He emptied the recycling bin before the garbage was collected.

   The waiter filled our empty water glasses.

5. The patient was resting comfortably when the doctor came to check on her.

   You can watch movies in the comfort of your home if you have the movie channel.

   I tried to comfort my friend, but I could not make her feel better.

   Are you comfortable in that chair, or would you like to sit in this one?

6. There are no vacancies in that apartment block.

   He stared vacantly into space during the boring lecture.

   You can study in this room; it's vacant until one o'clock.

   The students had to vacate the school during the fire drill.

Winnipeg
by Julia Kim

A.

1. Mr. Kim did not arrive in Winnipeg on January 23.

2. Julia and her daughters had to shorten their winter walk because it was very cold, and Julia was worried for her children.

3. After Julia and her daughters left the shopping mall, she couldn't remember where she had parked the car, and they spent one and a half hours trying to find it.

4. A police officer helped them find the car.

5. Julia's daughter enjoys looking at the sky.
6. They enjoy having snowball fights and skating outside.
7. Julia likes the fact that she can return books to other libraries.
8. Julia and her daughters enjoy cycling and rollerblading in the summer.
9. Julia describes Winnipeg as quiet, beautiful, and small.
10. Julia means that she is beginning to love Winnipeg and to feel comfortable here.

True or False?

1. F.
2. F.
3. T.
4. F.
5. T.

B. Vocabulary

Scrambled Words.

1. frozen
2. marshmallows
3. snowballs
4. library
5. apartment

Adjectives:

1. Apartments: differently shaped
2. Winnipeg: quiet, beautiful, and small
3. Villages: colorful
4. Brands: flashy, famous
5. How she feels in Winnipeg: quiet, clean, and cozy

Comparisons

1. The cold air entered the house like a baby rushing to its mummy.
2. The clouds were sweet and soft like marshmallows.
3. Winnipeg's sunny sky seems to resemble a watercolor painting.
4. The sky tells a story with clouds like a fairy tale book.
5. Julia plays with her daughters like friends.

Transit Drivers
by Souada Bauer

A.

1. An ambassador "to be" means someone who will become, or intends to become, an ambassador.
2. Souada describes the first type of bus driver as the patient type. The second one is the impatient type and the third one is the rare, security type. Finally, there's the speedy, eager type.
3. Souada is surprised that the bus driver can remember where the people want to get off the bus when there are so many traffic lights and stops.
4. The "security" type of bus driver checks every bus pass carefully.
5. A "power hour limit" is the 60 minute limit for using a bus transfer.
6. Souada was going to the College de St. Boniface to study French/ to take a refresher course in French.

B. Vocabulary

Matching

1. D
2. F

3. G
4. C
5. A
6. B
7. E

Fill in the Blanks

1. I prefer to buy local vegetables from Manitoba farmers.
2. When I'm upset, I often vent to my friends.
3. I don't believe him because he often fabricates stories.
4. We arrived at our final destination late last night.
5. Warm days are rare in Winnipeg in January.
6. I had a heart stopping experience the first time I tried down-hill skiing.
7. I wasn't paying attention, so I had only a vague idea of what the teacher was talking about.

Complete each phrase in the left column with the correct word in the right column.

1. E
2. D
3. A
4. C
5. B

Idioms and Expressions

1. How on earth do bus drivers remain so patient?
2. When I have nothing to say, I clam up.
3. His eagle eyes noticed everything.
4. I thought I'd lost my wallet, but lo and behold, I found it in my coat pocket!
5. He drove fast because he was on a mission to get to his class on time.

Window of Dreams

by Jamie Morales

A. Reading

1. F
2. T
3. T
4. F
5. T
6. F
7. T
8. T
9. T
10. T
11. T
12. F

1. Jamie is now 26 years old.
2. The "window of dreams" is the window that she is standing in front of in her condominium. It is a window that allows her to see where she is now and to look into her future.
3. Jamie says that she is eager to go to university, and to learn from her professors and classmates.

   She says that she strives for top marks, competing with students from all over the world.
4. She says that her mother still walks eleven blocks to work all year round to save money.
5. Jamie thinks that she has to have a car because it is too hard to ride the bus in -40 degree weather when she is carrying groceries.

6. Jamie has lost touch with some relatives because she is busy with her new life, and her relatives have gotten used to not having her there. As a result, they don't need her as much as they did before.

7. Jamie could not afford to buy a $1.25 drink at school at one time because her parents' expenses were greater than what they earned.

8. Jamie means that even though she and her family have made sacrifices, she appreciates the opportunities that she now has. She knows that the journey has been worthwhile, despite the pain and disappointment she has endured along the way.

B. Vocabulary

1. Protected: sheltered
2. Staring at: gazing at
3. Enthusiastic: eager
4. Without worries: carefree
5. The best grades: top marks
6. Hugs: embraces
7. Putting together: assembling
8. Relatives: kin
9. Ties between people: bonds
10. Careful with money: frugal

1. Many teenagers get their first job flipping hamburgers at a fast-food restaurant.
2. Juggling jobs isn't easy. You have to run from one part-time job to the next one.
3. When you enjoy your work, you find that time flies while you're at work.
4. Many immigrants have to work at two low-paying jobs just to make ends meet.

5. We all have our struggles in life, and we learn that life is not always a bowl of cherries

My Love, My Hero

Jay Sagin

Reading

A.

1. F
2. T
3. F
4. T
5. T

B. Vocabulary

Find the words in the story that have the same or similar meanings to the following words.

1. Give birth: bring my baby into the world
2. To be worried: to be concerned
3. Medication to help ease the pain: a painkiller
4. Instructed: directed
5. To protect: to guard

Word Families

Fill in the chart with the missing word forms. If there is an *x*, that particular word form does not exist.

	Noun	Verb	Adjective	Adverb
1	*pain, painkiller*	*to pain*	*painful*	*painfully*
2	*movement*	*to move*	*moved/moving*	x
3	*expenses*	x	*expensive*	*expensively*
4	*creation*	*to create*	*creative*	*creatively*
5	*concern*	*to concern*	*concerned*	x

Now, check your answers, and use the various words from the chart to fill in the blanks below.

1. He took a painkiller because he had a pain in his chest.
   It pained me to read about wars in our world.
   The poor young man was painfully shy.

2. The baby started to move, and I felt the movement as I placed my hand on my wife's belly.
   I was moved by the kindness that the stranger showed to me.

3. He dresses expensively! Did you see that expensive suit that he's wearing?
   They watched their expenses carefully as they saved to buy a house.

4. That artist has created a masterpiece.
   He is taking a creative writing course this year.
   She answered the questions very creatively!

5. The doctor was concerned about his patient's health.
   I have a concern about my grade on this exam.
   Please don't ask me any questions; this matter doesn't concern you

El Dorado
by Nina Singh

A.

Find the lines in the story that indicate the following.

1. The ruler of the Golden City was well liked. Their ruler was so favored that he was given precious gifts from Kings all over the world.

2. The little girl's eyes were different from her mother's eyes. Her mother had given her replicas of every part of herself, except for her eyes.

3. The girl's eyes were blue. The only thing they matched was the ocean, whose water reflected the blue skies that lingered above.

4. The girl wanted to visit the Golden City. The little girl vowed that one day she too would go to that place.

5. The tower where the girl's family lived was crowded. There were so many people crammed into every twist and turn.

6. Some of the people in the tower began to communicate with each other. They started to understand each other's language and value their beliefs.

7. Women went searching for their lost husbands. Many wives went by the ocean's edge every day for the rest of their lives hoping they would see the familiar face that never came.

8. The girl regrets her decision to come to "that place." I wish I had never come.

What is meant by the following phrases, or what is the author making a reference to?

1. This means that the Golden City was fascinating and attractive to the girl because she hadn't yet been there.

2. This means that the little girl chose not to listen to everything her mother said. She chose only what she wanted to hear.

3. This means that the people were needed to do the jobs that nobody else wanted to do.

4. These are the ghosts of the people who died when a nuclear bomb was dropped on the city of Nagasaki, Japan, at the end of World War II.

5. This means that you are not allowed to get on the bus unless you have the exact amount of money to pay for your bus fare.

B. Vocabulary

Match each word on the right with its meaning or synonym on the left.

1. E
2. H
3. B
4. D
5. L
6. I
7. A
8. K
9. F
10. C
11. J
12. G

Adjectives

1. finest foods
2. velvet red
3. exotic empress
4. undiscovered jewel
5. magnificent tower
6. incessant babbling
7. enchanted kingdom
8. horrifying reality
9. dirty work
10. restless souls
11. merciless sea
12. fiendish concoction
13. abandoned motherland

14. dark room
15. decaying tower, hopeless babblers
16. familiar face
17. gilded buildings
18. diseased or defective (body)
19. silly daydreaming
20. true story

Using Prepositions

1. to
2. of
3. off
4. of
5. from
6. of
7. out in
8. for
9. on
10. from
11. of
12. with
13. out of

Canadian Sonata
by Sergio Roysen

Reading

Note: Because this is a poem, there can certainly be other interpretations of the lines in the poem.

These answers are only suggestions of how the poem can be interpreted.

1. The words "Home. The Map. Easy definition" can mean that it is easy to locate our home country/city/town on the map; "Impossible task" implies that it is impossible to sum up exactly what "home" means to us.

2. Perhaps he uses the chest because our heart (which is associated with feelings and emotions) is in our chest. He may have used the right side of the brain because all of our creative thoughts come from that side of the brain. Finally, he mentions fists because we make a fist when we are ready to strike out at someone, or when we are feeling strong emotions. Thoughts, feelings and emotions come out at a time when we think of our home.

3. Sergio may be referring to something that we need in our lives. This is something that we feel deeply about and must create for ourselves and fight for.

4. Some things that Sergio describes that are impossible to do:
   - look through a wall
   - smell the wind that isn't blowing
   - chain yourself to a cloud and fly
   - touch the shadow of the night

5. When Sergio says "it's worth it", he may mean that leaving your country and coming to another one is really worth it.

6. The tremors Sergio refers to may be the fear and anxiety people feel when they are coming to a new place. He advises people to get rid of these feelings and face the future

True Love
by Nancy Repiso

A. Reading

True and False

1. F
2. F
3. T
4. F
5. T
6. F
7. T
8. F
9. T
10. F
11. F
12. T

Find the lines in the story that give the following information.

1. Nancy became a better person as a result of living away from home. **....a lot of life's learning happened. With it came experiences I am thankful for because they made me stronger, more aware, and sensitive to others' feelings. They helped me stand on my own and believe in myself.**

2. She realized that her life was incomplete without a partner. **I was missing that special someone with whom I would spend the rest of my life.**

3. The characteristics of a partner that she had originally thought were important were not really very important. **But my few years of living in Canada made me realize that finding someone with those qualities wasn't what would make our relationship last forever. I realized that those qualities were just the outer part of a person. My perception suddenly changed.**

4. Nancy and Edwin talked about more than just the good things that were happening in their lives. **Edwin and I shared our ups and downs.**

5. Nancy wasn't positive that their long distance relationship could last. **I did think that a long distance relationship might not work out, especially considering that we had never met each other.**

6. Edwin proposed to Nancy through social media. **There was a small yellow paper bag that he specifically told me to open in front of him via Skype. I was shocked and speechless when I saw what was inside the box. It was a ring. Then he immediately said what every woman desires to hear when they fall in love. "Will you marry me?"**

7. Nancy plans to have a religious marriage ceremony. **I will be standing in a sacred place filled with music, flowers and decorations.**

Matching

1. D
2. I
3. L
4. E
5. J
6. H
7. B
8. G
9. C
10. A
11. F
12. K

Note: Other answers may be correct, but this is the way these expressions appear in the story.

B. Vocabulary

1. When you care about how other people feel, you are sensitive to them.

2. When you know someone well, you can establish a relationship with that person.

3. To be ready for a big race, you have to condition yourself for it.

4. The way you see or view things is your perception of things.

5. Facebook is an example of a social network .

6. When you really care about what another person thinks, you value that person's opinion.

7. Two people living in two different countries can develop a(n) long distance relationship.

8. A serious relationship should be based on a strong foundation.

9. If you are determined, you can often conquer your fears.

10. Sometimes you have to take a risk, even if you're not sure you will succeed.

Word Families

	Noun	Verb	Adjective	Adverb
1	emotion	x	emotional	emotionally
2	sensitivity	to sensitize / to desensitize	sensitive	sensitively
3	value	to value/devalue	valuable	valuably
4	risk	to risk	risky	x
5	relationship	to relate	related	x

1. He couldn't hide his emotions when he found out that he had won the contest.

   It was such an emotional experience for him.

   He spoke emotionally of his love for his family.

2. The sensitive little girl cried when her friend teased her.

   Everyone was aware of the sensitivity of the situation.

They knew that the matter had to be handled sensitively.
Parents must sensitize their children to the feelings of
others.

3. I value you as a friend.

   Their currency has recently been devalued.

   He has made a valuable contribution to the team this year.

4. I don't want to risk losing my money in that scheme.

   Many people avoid gambling because they don't want to
   take a risk/risks with their money.

   Skiing down that high mountain looks too risky for me.

5. She and her parents have a wonderful relationship.

   You two must be related; you look so much alike.

   That teacher relates very well to her students.

Missing Words

1. to
2. as
3. for
4. in
5. for
6. as
7. for
8. in
9. in
10. of
11. of
12. for

More than an Immigrant: the remaking of self within a culture of silence

by German Cruz Reyes

A. Reading

1. German says that he was naive when he first came to Canada because he thought that it wouldn't be so hard to live in another culture.

2. He is still concerned about how he speaks English.

3. People condescended to German when they spoke to him by speaking slowly or looked at his wife instead of him when they spoke.

4. He felt that he had to learn English quickly because he needed a job.

5. German's warehouse job was stressful because everyone there was stressed out trying to meet the productivity quotas, and the supervisor kept pushing and reminding workers like German that they were still on probation.

6. He didn't quit his job because his wife was going to have a baby. He wanted to be provide for his family and be a good husband and father.

7. He felt "angry, humiliated, abused and exploited" when he got laid off one day before his six month probation time was due. He was told that maybe he wasn't the right person for the job.

8. German found out later that the company did this sort of thing all the time. They hired immigrants, made them work hard by threatening them with failing their probation, then gave the contract to another employee.

9. German has experienced a "culture of silence" in the schools and even when he's out for dinners with friends.

10. The type of racism that German has observed is stressful because it is not open or politically correct to say something against another culture.

11. According to German, segregation occurs when racism between immigrant groups perpetuates inequalities prescribed by the dominant culture and legitimizes the supposed superiority of one culture over another.

12. To have a positive cultural experience, German thinks that we must all see the things we have in common and celebrate the differences that make us unique and rich as a culture.

13. Seeing people from all over the world with different backgrounds living in relative harmony was what impressed him when he came to Winnipeg.

14. When he went back to Mexico, he realized that living in Canada had changed him, and he felt that he could no longer live in his homeland. He felt that both Canada and Mexico were both part of his cultural identity.

15. German believes that "the puzzle" that was once together falls to pieces and is all over the place when people immigrate to another country.

16. According to German, immigrants have to realize and accept that once they come to another country, they are different. They are no longer the same person with the same ideas and values.

17. We have no control over where we are born, but we can choose what and where we want to be.

Find the following lines in German's story and explain what he means when he makes these statements.

1. "No big deal everything is the same no matter where you live."

   When German says this, he means that it should not be difficult to adapt to a new culture because it can't be that different from his own.

2. "My worries of living here...took me out of my comfort zone."

German began to feel uncomfortable because there were aspects of living in another culture, such as being able to communicate well, that made him feel uncomfortable.

3. "I could feel it in the energy."

   At work, there was a "negative energy" because so many workers were stressed out by the supervisor, who was pushing them to make their productivity quotas and reminding some that they were still on probation in the warehouse. As a result, it was a hostile environment to work in.

4. "It was the most vulnerable time in my life."

   German was isolated, he had no community for support and no English to express himself, and his wife was expecting a baby. Therefore, he was powerless to speak up about the conditions at work, and he felt very vulnerable.

5. "Racism is hiding within the culture of silence."

   Racism is not out in the open; it isn't seen in physical violence. However, it exists in more subtle ways and is hidden under a culture of silence because people don't want to think that it exists here.

6. "When you move to another country, the puzzle that you relatively had together, is now all over the place."

   When you are living in another country, you feel as though the pieces of the puzzle that represents your life are no longer all together, and you have to put them all back together in a different way because they don't fit together the way they did before.

7. "We make Canada and Canada makes us."

   German means that immigrants contribute to the cultural makeup of Canada, making it richer for being a muticultural nation. In turn, Canada has an influence on immigrants, making their lives richer and shaping them into people with different ideas and values from the ones they had before they immigrated.

B. Vocabulary

Matching opposites.

1. D
2. E
3. F
4. H
5. B
6. I
7. A
8. J
9. G
10. C

Matching two parts of a phrase.

1. H
2. F
3. G
4. I
5. B
6. C
7. M
8. K
9. A
10. N
11. O
12. E
13. L
14. J
15. D

1. Because of his **limited English,** the immigrant to Canada had trouble expressing himself well.
2. I was out of my **comfort zone** in that awkward situation.
3. Usually, I have an **optimistic attitude,** but today I'm feeling rather negative.
4. In Canada, we are expected to be as **politically correct** as possible.
5. It is very difficult to do your job well in a hostile **work environment.**
6. I wasn't feeling happy, but I had to put on a **forced smile** in front of my friends.
7. People who act superior can give others an **inferiority complex.**
8. We sometimes feel jealous of others; it's just **human nature** to feel that way.
9. Peace-loving people try to avoid **physical violence.**
10. Unfortunately, in a multicultural society, **culture clashes** sometimes occur.
11. Which is the **dominant culture** in this country?
12. A country that is made up of people from many different cultures is certainly **culturally rich.**

Word Groups

1. **-ance/-ence** (6): tolerance/ circumstance/ experience/ violence/ silence/ difference

   These words are nouns, although experience and silence can also be verbs. Ex: to experience something/to silence a crowd

2. **-ant/-ent** (4): immigrant/ dominant/ incident/ different

   Immigrant and incident are nouns; dominant and different are adjectives.

3. **-tion** (14): implication/ connotation/ situation/ probation/ protection/ discrimination/colonization/ segregation/ preconception/ mention/ frustration/ option/ exploitation/ intention

   These words are nouns, although mention can also be a verb. Ex. He didn't mention the people who had received honourable mention in the contest.

4. **-ive** (4): aggressive/ manipulative / positive

   These words are adjectives.

5. **-able** (4): understandable/ vulnerable/ miserable/ uncomfortable

   These words are adjectives.

6. **-ity** (8): productivity/ superiority/ inferiority/ community/ reality/ identity/ opportunity/personality

   These words are nouns, but they can be used as adjectives. Ex: an inferiority complex, a personality trait.

7. **-ment** (4): environment/ apartment/ disappointment/ statement

   These words are nouns.

8. **-al** (6): general/ external/ cultural/ multicultural/ physical/ personal

   These words are adjectives. General can also be used as a noun. Ex: He was a general in the army.

9. **-ful** (3): wonderful/ stressful/ beautiful

   These words are adjectives.

10. **-ic** (2): intrinsic/optimistic

Use words from each numbered set of words to fill in the blanks in the following exercise.

1. **-ance/-ence**

   There is a great **difference** between his **circumstances** and yours because he has had many different **experiences** in his life.

2. **-ant/-ent**

   The life of an **immigrant** is often quite **different** from the life of those who belong to the **dominant** culture.

3. **-tion**

   Did he **mention** he has experienced **segregation, discrimination,** and **exploitation?**

4. **-ive**

   He works with an **aggressive** and **manipulative** boss. He feels so unhappy!

5. **-able**

   It's **understandable** that he feels so **vulnerable, miserable,** and **uncomfortable** in his workplace.

6. **-ity**

   The **reality** of the situation is there is no **opportunity** for him to be promoted in his workplace. As a result, he has developed feelings of **inferiority.**

7. **-ment**

   In his **statement** to his employees, the manager expressed his **disappointment** about their lack of concern for the **environment.**

8. **-al**

   In a **multicultural** country, can people retain their **cultural** identity?

9. **-ful**

   His life with his **beautiful** wife was far from **wonderful;** in fact, it was very **stressful** because he could never make her happy.

10. **-ic**

    He had an **intrinsic** desire to be **optimistic** in life.

Spirits of the North
by Faisal Islam

Reading

1. He took a canoe trip at night so that he could see the northern lights.

2. The body was made of birch, the resin for sealing the joints was from the pine tree, and the ribs and gunwales were made of white cedar.

3. The "more distant performers" were most likely the stars and/or the northern lights.

4. There are a few clues to indicate that Fred is probably Aboriginal. First of all, many northern guides are Aboriginal; also, Fred was chanting in Cree or Chipewyan, which are native languages. In addition, Fred's father made the canoe; it is mostly Aboriginal people who have the skills to make a canoe.

5. Faisal refers to the spot as "this sacred place" because he is in awe of what he has seen there.

He says that even the pictures he took could not convey the intensity and beauty of what he experienced. As well, Fred looked spellbound and possessed by what he saw at this special place.

A. Vocabulary

1. M
2. E
3. Q
4. N
5. J
6. F
7. G
8. L

9. B
10. I
11. P
12. D
13. O
14. R
15. A
16. S
17. H
18. T
19. C
20. K

B.

1. grin
2. jetty
3. emerge
4. stellar
5. shattered
6. blanketed
7. grandeur
8. gear
9. randomly
10. remote

C.

1. faded away, pack up
2. load up, head for
3. pointed out, make out
4. take in, focus on
5. come back, book in

A Better Place
by Gentil Misigaro

Reading
Read the lyrics to the song and answer the following questions.

1. Gentil feels that the following things are missing from his life: joy, excitement, comfort, (hope of) freedom, justice, and love.

2. When he has these things, the brightness and sunshine will return to his life.

3. The two comparisons in the second verse of the song are "Walking like a lion in a jungle" and "Flying like an eagle when the sky is blue."

4. The lion comparison represents a feeling of pride, and the eagle comparison represents a feeling of freedom.

5. The opposites are:

   a. love

   b. peace

   c. justice

   d. joy

   e. hope

   f. sorrow

After Reading

B.

1. H
2. F
3. C
4. I
5. G
6. A
7. J
8. E
9. D
10. B

Word Searches and Crossword Puzzles

The word searches and crossword puzzles in this section are a fun way to review the vocabulary from the stories, song, and poem that you have read. Each word search and puzzle contains vocabulary from three selections in the book.

You should do the word search first. Remember that the words you are searching for can appear across, down, and diagonally on the grid. They may also be spelled backwards! It is best to do the word search before you do the crossword puzzle. It you get stuck when you are doing the crossword puzzle, check the list of words in the corresponding word search. All the words that you need to complete the crossword puzzle should be listed there.

Good luck, and have fun reviewing your vocabulary!

Word search

A Place Called Home, The Beginning, Winnipeg

```
L  J  O  J  C  Y  X  S  Q  K  O  G  E  Q  R  S  G  F  S  E
M  H  Q  E  W  E  B  T  M  P  Q  C  B  E  L  R  A  U  E  U
V  K  I  Z  G  V  F  B  C  E  A  C  T  A  A  R  M  X  K  Q
M  A  J  O  R  I  T  Y  O  R  G  N  D  D  E  P  Y  K  A  I
R  G  W  I  R  D  F  L  B  H  U  N  U  W  T  C  T  D  F  N
E  E  H  X  D  L  E  M  Y  O  A  A  E  U  M  I  I  V  X  U
D  V  Z  M  X  A  E  L  C  S  T  L  O  A  A  N  N  M  V  Z
G  Y  I  V  X  P  V  N  U  E  L  U  J  O  N  A  R  J  S  L
T  N  A  C  A  V  E  E  U  S  S  R  C  V  S  G  E  K  L  Y
V  A  N  Q  U  I  S  H  H  G  I  D  M  M  I  R  T  L  L  Z
C  U  R  I  O  S  I  T  Y  Y  E  O  R  L  O  O  E  L  Z  P
O  E  C  I  L  T  Y  O  T  A  V  D  N  A  N  D  E  P  Y  W
M  A  R  S  H  M  A  L  L  O  W  S  A  A  W  B  N  F  B  H
E  L  B  B  E  P  V  F  P  U  E  Q  Z  R  L  K  T  S  O  K
E  Y  M  Q  I  M  G  J  G  Q  J  R  T  P  E  E  W  A  Z  F
L  M  W  J  B  S  G  A  A  L  L  M  H  E  K  U  R  A  S  U
J  J  Q  L  I  D  R  R  U  K  B  J  M  C  R  S  Q  E  O  F
X  O  B  F  E  J  F  I  I  P  W  V  I  S  E  G  Y  S  H  E
A  K  I  G  R  G  N  P  W  U  Q  H  J  P  Z  I  E  V  A  W
M  C  U  K  Z  N  V  K  R  R  T  C  R  X  W  Z  Y  R  M  M
```

AWKWARD	BELLY	CURIOSITY
DELUSIONAL	DEW	EMBRACE
ENCOUNTER	ETERNITY	FAKE
FAREWELL	GEMS	GRADUATE
HOARSE	HOBBY	MAJORITY
MANSION	MARSHMALLOWS	MASQUERADE
ORGANIC	PEBBLE	REGRET
SANDALS	SUMPTUOUS	THICKET
UNIQUE	VACANT	VANQUISH

Across
2. uncomfortable
3. forever
5. the name for food that is grown naturallyl, without chemicals
8. the opposite of minority
10. suffering from delusions
11. a party where everyone wears a mask
14. jewels
16. moisture that appears on the grass and flowers in the morning
18. a children's story full of imagination
19. one of a kind
21. they are soft and white, and they are often toasted over a campfire
26. meet
27. noun from the adjective curious

Down
1. a huge, expensive house
4. Do you _____ your decision to immigrate?
6. conquer
7. to successfully finish high school or university
9. not real
12. to hug or kiss someone
13. stomach
15. goodbye
17. open shoes that are worn in the summer
20. something that you enjoy doing in your spare time
22. extravagant
23. a popular winter sport in Canada
24. empty
25. a smooth, round stone

Word search solution

A Place Called Home, The Beginning, Winnipeg

AWKWARD	BELLY	CURIOSITY
DELUSIONAL	DEW	EMBRACE
ENCOUNTER	ETERNITY	FAKE
FAREWELL	GEMS	GRADUATE
HOARSE	HOBBY	MAJORITY
MANSION	MARSHMALLOWS	MASQUERADE
ORGANIC	PEBBLE	REGRET
SANDALS	SUMPTUOUS	THICKET
UNIQUE	VACANT	VANQUISH

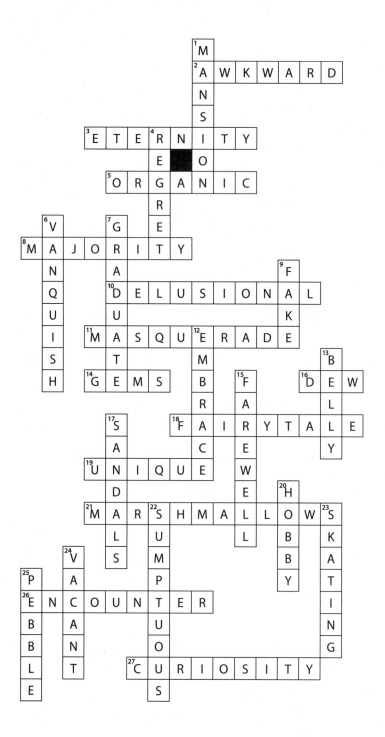

Word search

Transit Drivers, Window of Dreams, My Love

```
R L M T T D D E N E O A V A T I G S E C
E A K K N A Z Y Z H M P Q W W A R F X D
F D Y O O E R I R E L L I K N I A P I S
S E B R E E N A T O L M Z S X O E S A N
N M B U F I O N X J Y C H E Y V C C A H
A A Q L T L A C I L I B M U I O R I N K
R S E U S X I F A Z B A Y R U I V M X P
T C R X Q L N C K P R P T R F E X H X Z
T C Y P B Q E B U F E S A I W H A Y G M
S Z T V P U V E F T B G C Q D T V H O W
S D R Q T Y I E T J E E S U O E G R O G
P C E F O H T V L A S D E N R E C N O C
E S V C X U A P G B C F O R T U N A T E
X J O H H S B L U R M I E R I M D A F I
E T P Q M U L Z U L V E R M H V X Z P S
M A E R C S E A A P W A S B A E X G P G
O P P O R T U N I T I E S S A D C E O Z
L S A Y X Q Q F D B F Z K T A F E T W F
D Y Q C G P O P C C F Q C Y J D G D I H
H A S L L T E D L X L M I T Y R T X D C
```

ABROAD	ADMIRE	ASSEMBLE
BOND	CONCERNED	DISCOURAGE
FABRICATE	FOG	FORTUNATE
GORGEOUS	HECTIC	INEVITABLE
MEDAL	NAÏVE	OPPORTUNITIES
PAINKILLER	POVERTY	REFLECT
SACRIFICES	SCREAM	SCRUTINIZE
SPEEDY	SQUEEZE	STRIVE
TRANSFER	UMBILICAL	

Across
1. a very heavy mist
3. to change from one bus to another
6. slang expression that means be quiet
10. examine very closely
12. the things we give up in order to get something that we really want
15. lucky
16. the baby's _____ chord must be cut at birth
18. _____ people believe everything they are told
21. overseas
23. extremely busy
24. put together
25. really fast

Down
2. chances
4. really beautiful
5. the opposite of encourage
7. medication taken to reduce pain
8. to think highly of someone or something
9. yell
11. an award given to Olympic athletes
12. hold on very tightly
13. worried
14. to work hard for something = to _____ for it
15. to make something up
17. bound to happen, unpreventable
19. noun from the adjective "poor"
20. to think deeply about = to _____ on
22. to form a close relationship

Word search solution

Transit Drivers, Window of Dreams, My Love

ABROAD	ADMIRE	ASSEMBLE
BOND	CONCERNED	DISCOURAGE
FABRICATE	FOG	FORTUNATE
GORGEOUS	HECTIC	INEVITABLE
MEDAL	NAÏVE	OPPORTUNITIES
PAINKILLER	POVERTY	REFLECT
SACRIFICES	SCREAM	SCRUTINIZE
SPEEDY	SQUEEZE	STRIVE
TRANSFER	UMBILICAL	

Word search

El Dorado, Canadian Sonata, True Love

```
L  F  U  T  O  C  R  U  D  Q  G  S  E  D  G
Q  Z  O  A  N  E  I  E  S  N  M  N  L  E  N
B  U  N  U  T  E  T  T  I  N  I  A  A  F  I
E  K  A  T  N  I  S  H  O  N  K  I  H  E  Y
G  X  I  L  O  D  C  B  C  X  D  R  N  C  A
E  L  H  L  I  A  A  E  A  E  E  A  I  T  C
G  U  P  A  O  T  S  T  C  A  E  B  N  I  E
P  X  L  R  L  S  I  I  I  J  A  R  O  V  D
E  H  P  A  A  E  P  E  B  O  X  A  I  E  T
S  P  J  N  V  H  Q  C  S  W  N  B  T  S  S
A  E  T  W  E  M  A  G  I  C  A  L  I  K  U
E  Y  D  R  H  S  I  D  N  E  I  F  D  Y  N
D  E  T  A  C  H  E  D  Q  N  O  Z  N  P  A
A  D  V  A  N  C  E  P  X  X  T  F  O  E  M
H  C  T  I  W  E  B  O  O  U  D  V  C  V  I
```

ABSENT	ADVANCE	APPROACHING
BARBARIANS	BEWITCH	CONDITION
DECAYING	DECIPHER	DEFECTIVE
DETACHED	DYE	EXHALE
EXOTIC	EXPLOITED	FIENDISH
FOUNDATION	GLITTER	INCESSANT
INHALE	MAGICAL	QUALITIES
SKYPE	TSUNAMI	VALUE

Across

3. breathe in
8. a base
11. not working properly, faulty
14. a modern way by which people can communicate face-to-face electronically
15. painted with a thin layer of gold
16. separated from
18. the opposite of refined people
19. the opposite of present
20. a natural disaster involving earth tremors
22. rotting, falling apart
23. admire, think highly of
24. opposite of ordinary
25. to prepare oneself for something = to _____ oneself for it
26. full of magic

Down

1. to move forward, make progress
2. breathe out
4. used for one's own advantage
5. a natural disaster that involves extremely high waves of water
6. characteristics
7. to cast a magical spell over
9. to change colour of
10. to protect
12. horrendous, extremely mean
13. endless
14. frightened
15. sparkle
17. to figure out
19. coming close to
21. holy, religious

Word search solution

El Dorado, Canadian Sonata, True Love

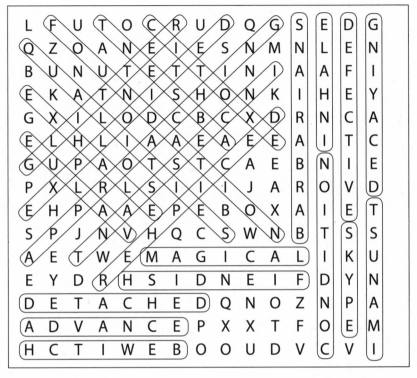

ABSENT	ADVANCE	APPROACHING
BARBARIANS	BEWITCH	CONDITION
DECAYING	DECIPHER	DEFECTIVE
DETACHED	DYE	EXHALE
EXOTIC	EXPLOITED	FIENDISH
FOUNDATION	GLITTER	INCESSANT
INHALE	MAGICAL	QUALITIES
SKYPE	TSUNAMI	VALUE

Word search

More than Immigrant, Spirits, A Better Place

```
N D E C Q R P Z E Y H G E G S U J I O W
T E E C I D A W H T Y T U N P N D M T I
K O G G A T X N E Q O D B I E C C P C S
Y D L A A E S G D M A M D D L O H L S H
U T A E T L P I E O X A N N L N A I E I
D H I Q R I F R M N M O Q E B S N C R N
Y I B T S A V U R I I L G C O C T I P G
J H I G N U N E O T T E Y S U I I T E X
U C R P Y E G C P M X P T E N O N E N Q
N A C Y M N D E E C A N O D D U G I T H
G N H H I A C I L E A C H K S S B S O G
L O N S Q N I U Z N E A J O H L I S U I
E E S S O N D I I A R L R R L Y T Q F M
U I C C R E L M F M P R D N A I O T W M
M Z E U D A O X O Z O Y I D L E W P T E
D R Q K E D D N U W O K X E A E R J H N
P S U R V N Y M S I C A R P S P O O Z S
M L E R Y T O U A S M W M F I M J K O E
I U R H U U B M Q I I Y J W W C A Z C E
P M X Z Q H W I J D M C J F D T M T J C
```

BIRCH	CAMOUFLAGED	CANOE
CHANTING	DESCENDING	DOMINANT
EXCLUDED	HARMONY	HOSTILE
IDENTITY	IMMENSE	IMPLICIT
JUNGLE	MAJOR	MISSING
NEGATIVE	OPTIMISTIC	PADDLE
PEACE	PRECONCEPTION	RACISM
RANDOMLY	REALIZE	REMOTE
SERPENT	SORROW	SPELLBOUND
TOLERANCE	UNCONSCIOUSLY	WISHING

Across

3. the opposite of explicit
4. a type of water transportation originally used by the aborginal people
7. extremely unfriendly
9. to be aware of
11. discrimination against a certain group of people or culture
14. a form of aboriginal singing
16. hoping
18. the opposite of minor
20. the noun form of the verb to tolerate
24. without knowing or being aware of
29. hidden, blending in with the surroundings

Down

1. the natural habitat of tigers and lions
2. the wood used in making canoes
5. coming down
6. huge
8. bewitched, in a trance
10. the opposite of pessimistic
11. without a set pattern
12. the opposite of war
13. snake
15. the opposite of positive
17. extreme sadness
19. far away, isolated
21. a wooden oar used to move a canoe through the water
23. The _____ child still hasn't been found
25. an idea that is formed before one has accumulated all the facts
26. opposite of included
27. the opposite of discord
28. some people lose their cultural _____ when they move to another country.

Word search solution

More than Immigrant, Spirits, A Better Place

BIRCH	CAMOUFLAGED	CANOE
CHANTING	DESCENDING	DOMINANT
EXCLUDED	HARMONY	HOSTILE
IDENTITY	IMMENSE	IMPLICIT
JUNGLE	MAJOR	MISSING
NEGATIVE	OPTIMISTIC	PADDLE
PEACE	PRECONCEPTION	RACISM
RANDOMLY	REALIZE	REMOTE
SERPENT	SORROW	SPELLBOUND
TOLERANCE	UNCONSCIOUSLY	WISHING